FROM CELL TO TEST TUBE

THE SCIENCE OF BIOCHEMISTRY

From Cell to Test Tube

THE SCIENCE OF BIOCHEMISTRY

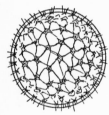

by Robert Warner Chambers, Ph.D.

and Alma Smith Payne, M.A.

DRAWINGS BY LILLI MAUTNER

CHARLES SCRIBNER'S SONS, *New York*

Preface

BIOCHEMISTRY AFFECTS the lives of every one of us with increasing importance every day. Yet students interested in careers in science, teachers, counselors, and the general public know very little about this relatively new and exciting science. Occasionally writers for slick magazines and Sunday supplements point out some of its practical applications, but the material is most frequently presented from a medical point of view rather than from the standpoint of biochemistry as a science in its own right. So biochemistry continues to wear its brilliant accomplishments under several different disguises and all too seldom is given the credit it deserves.

This book provides an introduction to biochemistry for the layman. We have tried to explain important biochemical concepts in terms which the general reader with limited or no scientific background can understand. In order to do this we have eliminated chemical symbols, mathematical equations, and other such tools of the trade. We have kept biochemical jargon to a minimum, but complete elimination of these terms seemed undesirable since they are appearing with increasing frequency in newspaper and magazine articles. Where these terms are used we have tried to define them clearly.

In order to emphasize that biochemistry, like any other science, depends upon research for progress, we have included descriptions

v

of some of the important experiments which established certain biochemical concepts. We have also used historical material to illustrate the long and twisting and often irregular trail of research which almost invariably precedes a great discovery. Finally, we have included some of the practical applications of this hard-won biochemical knowledge to illustrate the importance of biochemistry to modern living.

The reader should recognize that the material presented in this book represents only a small part of the information which is available in the rapidly expanding science of biochemistry. Our choice of subject matter was influenced by our desire to tell the story of biochemistry as simply as possible and at the same time to illustrate the wide scope of this science. Therefore, it was necessary to select those concepts which best fitted these requirements. It was also necessary to choose a few experiments (among many important ones) and a few names (among many famous ones) to illustrate the story as we wanted to tell it.

Whether you are headed for a scientific career or are reading *From Cell to Test Tube* for general information, our hope is that this book will give you a clearer understanding of the value and scope of biochemistry and indicate some of the directions it may take as its promising future unfolds.

We would like to thank Dr. Robert C. Warner for his criticisms of the manuscript and his helpful suggestions. We are indebted to Dr. Alex B. Novikoff for permission to reproduce some of his cell drawings.

ROBERT WARNER CHAMBERS, PH.D.
Assistant Professor in Biochemistry
New York University College of Medicine

ALMA SMITH PAYNE, M.A.
Former Supervisor, *Berkeley Public Schools*
Berkeley, California

Contents

FROM CELL TO TEST TUBE

THE SCIENCE OF BIOCHEMISTRY

Chapter 1

BIOCHEMISTRY AND YOU

EVERY LIVING THING from man to microbe, plant or animal, is a complicated chemical machine. Biochemistry seeks to explain how this machine operates in terms of atoms and molecules—how it is put together, how it functions, and why it sometimes gets out of adjustment. As the name implies, then, biochemistry is biology at the chemical level.

We cannot hope to understand a machine without taking it apart. Lifting the hood of an automobile and looking at the motor doesn't tell us much about the engine. But remove the head from the engine block and we can see the valves and pistons. Then by carefully dismantling the motor, piece by piece, we can learn the relationship of each part to its neighbors; from this information we can gain considerable insight into how the engine works.

So it is with a living organism—one cannot hope to find out how it operates until the parts which compose it and their relationship to one another are known. However, instead of valves and pistons, the biochemist must deal with chemical substances.

Unfortunately, a living cell cannot be disassembled in an orderly manner. Once the thin membrane which surrounds the cell is broken, all the chemical substances spill out. Not only is the relationship of one substance to another *inside* the cell lost, but a complex mixture which is difficult to separate into component parts results. The situation is a little like taking an engine apart blindfolded, mixing up all the parts and then trying to reassemble the motor without any previous knowledge of where each part fits.

Even though the task has been difficult, biochemists have made a good deal of progress not only in determining the nature of the individual pieces which make up the cellular machine but how these parts work. For example, we know that, in addition to the carbohydrates, proteins and fats, which are characteristic of living organisms, there are a multitude of other substances inside the cell: salts, such as sodium chloride (table salt); minerals, such as iron; and a whole host of carbon-containing (organic) compounds, such as vitamin B_1 (thiamine). We also know how many of these compounds, such as vitamins, function; why proteins are so important; and so on.

Our knowledge of even the simplest organism is still far from complete, yet progress has been rapid considering the difficulties involved. Now more than ever biochemical research is pushing ahead at a rapid rate and many of the fruits of this work are known to all of us: antibiotics, such as penicillin; hormones, such as cortisone; valuable chemicals, such as citric acid; vaccines, such as the Salk polio vaccine. These are only a few of the modern miracles which have received a big assist from biochemistry. In reality its contributions to our lives are all around us. Yet most of us know very little about this science which affects our lives so much.

As an example of biochemistry's contribution to medicine consider the Salk polio vaccine. This vaccine is a mixture of the three strains of polio virus which cause paralytic forms of the disease. It is prepared from viruses which have been killed with formaldehyde so that when they are injected into our bodies they do not multiply and form new viruses as the live virus does. But the killed virus does call out the fighting troops of the body's defense forces. Special proteins called antibodies are produced—one type for each strain of polio virus. These antibodies remain in the blood and guard us against infection by live polio viruses. Should a live virus enter the body, the correct antibody combines with it and renders it harmless.

The trail of research which eventually led to the vaccine began in 1893 when Ivanovski, a Russian bacteriologist, discovered viruses. In an effort to find the cause of mosaic disease that killed tobacco plants, he ground up infected leaves and pressed out the sap. Then he passed the sap through the newly developed porcelain filter candles to remove the bacteria from the preparation. When the bacteria-free filtrate was rubbed on the leaves of healthy plants, mosaic disease appeared. A little later other diseases, such as polio (1902), were shown to be caused by viruses.

For a long time the nature of these infective agents, which were much too small to see with an ordinary microscope, eluded scientists. Then, as research progressed new techniques for studying the elusive viruses were developed and biochemists began to lay the foundation for our present knowledge. Eventually, with the use of a special kind of microscope, the *electron microscope,* it was possible to see individual virus particles. Tobacco mosaic virus looked like a cigarette with the paper peeled off, while certain bacteriophage (viruses which infect bacteria) resembled tiny tadpoles. All of these viruses produced disease and they all required a living host cell in order to grow and reproduce. Polio virus was particularly finicky. Man was the only natural host for it so it was most difficult to find adequate supplies for study. Finally, monkeys were infected with the virus, then cotton rats. Progress was being made but not enough. Large amounts of the virus were needed for vaccine production, and culturing the virus in living animals was impractical for this purpose.

The brilliant Harvard team of Enders, Weller, and Robbins effected the break-through with their development of a new technique for growing viruses in tissue cultures. First, they removed normal living cells from organisms and carefully nurtured them in bottles. The cells continued to live and grow in their artificial environment. Then they found that they could infect tissue cultures of kidney with polio virus and, as the kidney cells multiplied, they could continue to manufacture new virus. Here at last was a technique for producing enough virus to make a vaccine. This team was awarded the Nobel Prize in medicine and physiology in 1954 for their discovery that the poliomyelitis virus could be grown in tissue culture.

The actual preparation of the first vaccine for immunization against polio was developed by Dr. Jonas E. Salk

Electron microscope pictures of two types of viruses

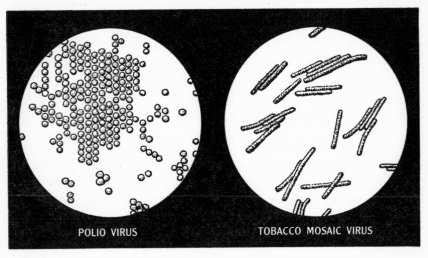

POLIO VIRUS   TOBACCO MOSAIC VIRUS

at the University of Pittsburgh Medical School. First, he grew the polio virus in tissue culture, using monkey tissue. Then using the knowledge handed down by such men as Stanley, he inactivated the virus by treating it with formaldehyde. Injection of the "killed" virus into healthy monkeys protected them from infection by live virus. Would it also protect humans? he wondered.

By the summer of 1956, among every 100,000 children who had received one or more shots of the Salk vaccine, the number of cases of paralytic polio averaged only 6.3, while among unvaccinated children the cases averaged 29.2. On the basis of these early figures a vaccinated child ran about one-fifth as much risk of getting paralytic polio as an unvaccinated child. Dr. Leonard A. Scheele, former Surgeon General of the United States, has said, "Unquestionably, we now have a vaccine which is standing up under most careful scrutiny with respect to safety and effectiveness." Dr. Salk had a satisfying answer.

Today, thanks to the effectiveness of this vaccine, polio is on the way out as a crippling disease. But virus research goes on. Many scientists believe that a "killed vaccine," such as the Salk vaccine, in which the ability of the virus to reproduce in the host cell is irrevocably destroyed, is not the final answer. Instead of inactivating the virus, it is often possible to change its biological properties so that it no longer causes disease. However, this attenuated virus can still multiply in suitable host cells. When a vaccine produced from the attenuated virus is injected into a healthy person it starts a complicated chain of events which protects him from the disease-producing virus. Perhaps an even more effective vaccine will be produced in this way.

There is still much to learn about polio virus and other viruses. Each new fact turned up by basic research in this field of investigation will advance man a step closer to the day when all virus disease will be a thing of the past.

Biochemistry has also helped to popularize the little organisms. For example, consider the tiny molds, which under a powerful microscope often appear as sprawling masses of threadlike fibers shaped like a gnarled root system. These microorganisms, as they are called, are everywhere about us—as mildew spots on citrus fruits, meats, stale bread, and other soft foods. Sometimes they appear as chamoislike pads floating on top of liquids which have been left unsealed and exposed to the air. The biochemist is interested in these molds not just as spoilage spots on foods but as living organisms. (See drawing of *Penicillium chrysogenum* on page 46.)

This curiosity about the nature of molds led to the industrial development of fermentation (the chemical reactions carried out by molds and bacteria) for the production of valuable chemicals, antibiotics, and hormones. This important application of biochemistry developed with the production of citric acid, in which the tiny green mold, *Aspergillus,* played a leading role.

Citric acid is used in a variety of ways. As an acidulant,

it gives a tang to foods and beverages. It is also used in dyes, inks, and silver plating. It helps to put the fizz in effervescent powders and tablets. In the field of cosmetics citric acid is the acid stabilizer in permanent wave solutions.

The commercial production of citric acid by fermentation was pioneered by Charles Pfizer and Co., Inc. For years citric acid was extracted from crude calcium citrate —a natural citrus product—which was imported from Italy and the West Indies. This method was not only costly, but the supply of raw material was subject to seasonal variations of the citrus crop.

"Surely there must be some better way to get citric acid," Pfizer scientists thought. "Many microorganisms produce small amounts of citric acid. Perhaps they can be coaxed to yield larger amounts."

To find out, they turned to a study of molds. First they examined all kinds of these little microorganisms to learn about their eating and living habits. Finally, after almost ten years of research, they perfected a process whereby the mold *Aspergillus niger,* a living organism, would transform sugar into citric acid by fermentation.

This resulted in the opening of the first citric acid fermentation plant in the world in 1927. The price of citric acid dropped from a dollar a pound to twenty-five cents. Suddenly the United States was in the export business rather than being an importer of this useful chemical. And the Pfizer Company became a world leader in fermentation chemistry. By perfecting the process of controlled fermentation, citric acid could be made in less than two weeks without regard to weather or crop yield.

It would take thousands and thousands of lemon and lime trees to yield the tons of citric acid which the Pfizer team of scientists and technologists now produce with their precious mold and molasses.

Industrial fermentation has also become a valuable method for producing drugs to alleviate the suffering of patients in many different disease states. For example, take arthritis. About eleven years ago scientists discovered that cortisone, a hormone liberated by the adrenal gland, markedly helped the symptoms of some patients suffering from rheumatoid arthritis. Overnight, a tremendous demand for cortisone developed. Its magic, however, received a big setback by the serious, sometimes dangerous, side-effects which some patients developed.

Biochemists went to work to meet the medical need and to abolish the danger of the hormone while keeping its healing properties. They knew that cortisone belonged to a group of chemical substances known as steroids. Many of these steroids, such as cholesterol and the bile salts, were close relatives of cortisone and were relatively easy to obtain from living tissues. The bile salts were first chosen as the raw material for cortisone because they could be obtained fairly easily from cattle. But it took thirty-seven separate chemical conversions to turn a single bile salt into cortisone. This was so wasteful of the starting material that it required about forty head of cattle to provide enough cortisone to treat one patient for one day. The process was time-consuming too, and consequently cortisone remained for some time almost prohibitively expensive.

Durey H. Peterson of the Upjohn Company in Kalamazoo, Michigan, decided to try to put microorganisms to work on this problem. He tested many different ones to see if any of them would introduce an oxygen atom at an appropriate position in the steroid molecule. None of them worked. However, one important member of the mold family, *Rhizopus,* was nowhere to be found in the laboratories. "Since we don't have *Rhizopus,* it is just the one that will probably do the trick," Peterson remarked with a touch of irony. "Let's get it."

The Upjohn researchers knew that even the relatively clean air of Kalamazoo was filled with the ever-present molds. So they placed a culture plate on a window sill and waited. As they expected, *Rhizopus* made its entrance. They isolated a pure culture of the mold and tested it. It worked. *Rhizopus* had accomplished in one step the conversion which had taken chemists more than a score of reactions.

Soon, not only cortisone but many related steroids which are useful in the treatment of such diseases as rheumatoid arthritis, disfiguring skin conditions, and certain allergies, such as asthma, were being prepared with submicroscopic organisms—and relatively easily too. Today cortisone has only limited use because some of its chemical relatives are safer and more effective in treating disease. But the Upjohn cortisone process was the first in which microorganisms were used to produce this type of steroid hormone. Similar techniques with other organisms have produced other important chemicals, such as penicillin and other antibiotics, which are now used to treat a variety of plant, animal, and human diseases.

As we can see, biochemistry has become more and more important. It has become a kind of jack-of-all-sciences, evolving from the union of many biological sciences with chemistry. Its foundation is built on research carried out by scientists who are curious about life and who believe that every gain, however small, is a gain in understanding it. These scientists in many different countries are giving us the biochemical concepts which have advanced man's understanding of living organisms to the point where we are able to describe them in considerable detail at the chemical level.

This book will tell you about some of these concepts—their origin and development—and will also describe some of the experiments which led to important discoveries. As the story of biochemistry unfolds, you will see what it is and how its accomplishments influence whatever we do wherever we are.

2

THE CELL MACHINE

THE CELL—a blob of jellylike *protoplasm* surrounded by a thin membrane—is the fundamental unit of life. Biochemistry seeks to explain the phenomenon of life in terms of the chemical reactions which go on inside the cell. To understand biochemistry, then, we need to know something about the cell structure of living organisms.

No one is sure when life began on the earth. But it was a long time ago—perhaps one and a half to two billion years ago. Nor do scientists know *how* life began. But it probably began in the sea.

One theory of the origin of life holds that powerful electrical discharges passing through the gases which surrounded the ancient earth produced a variety of new chemical compounds. These molecules dissolved in the sea and during the passage of millions of years more complicated molecules were formed. Somehow these chemical substances banded together and formed simple living organisms. How this occurred is a mystery, but by the pre-Cambrian era, more than five hundred million years ago, the oceans were teeming with tiny, single-celled creatures which were the ancestors of the plant and animal world of today.

We are not sure what these primitive organisms looked like because they were soft-bodied and so they left no clear fossil record. Probably they were little more than the blobs of jellylike material (called protoplasm), surrounded by a thin membrane. The protoplasm was mostly water, but it also contained the chemical substances essential for life. If these fragile creatures had been exposed to the barren land the heat of the sun would soon have dried them up and killed them. Furthermore, they couldn't move around very well on land and there was nothing for them to eat. And even these simple organisms had to eat. The seas contained a multitude of chemicals which they could "eat" and the water kept their protoplasm from drying out. So they lived in the sea.

Our present day amoeba may be a direct descendant of the ancient single-celled animals. It is a member of a large group of simple animal forms called protozoa. It is nothing more than a mass of protoplasm surrounded by a cell membrane, but it is a remarkably efficient organism. For example, the protoplasm in an amoeba flows around inside the cell membrane causing it to bulge out in what appear to be armlike projections. By changing its shape in this manner the amoeba can actually move about in water and can capture morsels of food.

Perhaps by chance, some of the single-celled organisms came together and formed colonies which were much more efficient than their single-celled ancestors. They thrived and became the forebears of the more complicated multi-cellular animals and plants which we know today. The colonylike protozoon, *volvox,* is similar to what scientists think some of the ancient cell colonies looked like.

As evolution progressed over millions of years, the complexity of these multicellular organisms changed and they became more specialized. Jellyfish with primitive mouths and stomachs developed. Worms with simple nervous systems and crude brains evolved. Eventually man made his appearance. Impossible, you say. How could a complicated human body develop from a simple, one-celled organism? But consider that man grows from a single cell (the fertilized egg) into trillions of highly specialized cells by time of birth—and all in the span of nine short months. In fact, from a biological point of view, man is nothing more than a collection of single cells which have specialized to perform the functions which his environment requires. In terms of the cells which compose the whole organism, man is not so different from an amoeba after all.

It took scientists a long time to recognize the importance of the cell as a unit of life because most cells were

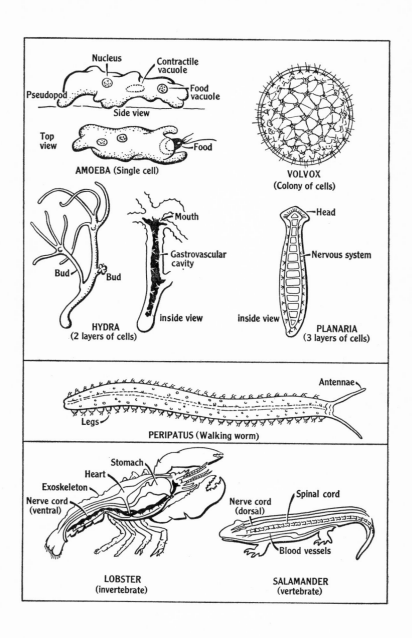

difficult to study. Actually, our understanding of cell structure paralleled the development of a very important piece of laboratory equipment—the microscope.

Even the name *cell* came from the seventeenth-century experiments of Robert Hooke, an English experimental physicist. Hooke, the first curator of experiments for the Royal Society in London, was fascinated with the newly developed microscope. One day he sliced a thin piece of cork and examined it under the microscope. To his astonishment, he found that it was composed of neatly arranged rows of holes or cavities. Each of these cavities was enclosed by walls which reminded him of the row of bare rooms or cells in which monks lived in their monasteries. So he named the cork holes *cells*. But Hooke didn't realize that the most important part of the cells was missing—the protoplasm. He saw only the empty cavities which had once contained active, living protoplasm.

At about this same time, Anton van Leeuwenhoek, a Dutch dry goods merchant and part-time janitor, made some remarkable observations. Leeuwenhoek's hobby was grinding bits of glass into powerful lenses. In his attic laboratory he perfected his technique so that he was able to magnify objects as much as 270 times. These magnificent lenses, mounted in a simple metal holder, formed the simple microscopes which he used to observe the sub-visible world about him.

Leeuwenhoek's skill was so great that his simple instruments were far superior to the more complicated, but less well-made, compound microscope which Hooke used on his cell observations.

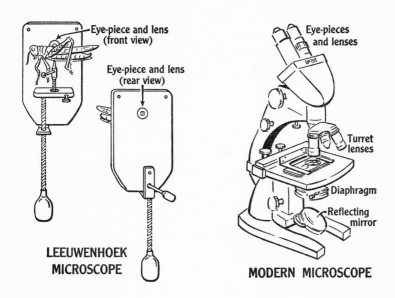

Eye-piece and lens
(front view)

Eye-piece and lens
(rear view)

Eye-pieces
and lenses

Turret
lenses

Diaphragm

Reflecting
mirror

**LEEUWENHOEK
MICROSCOPE**

MODERN MICROSCOPE

Leeuwenhoek turned his glasses on everything about him and saw blood circulating through the tiny vessels in the tail of a fish; a bee stinger; the brain of a fly; the hair on his own body, to name only a few of his discoveries. But these observations were merely a prelude to his most exciting discovery.

Leeuwenhoek was a curious man and he wondered what pure water would look like under magnification. He had seen all kinds of squirming life forms in putrid water, but would they be present in "pure" water? To find out he set an earthen pot in the garden to catch rain water. When it filled he removed a tiny drop and fastened it onto the needle of his microscope.

He couldn't believe what he saw and called to his daughter to join him. "See what I see, Maria. There are little animals in this rain water. Can you see them, too? They are swimming and playing around in the water. Just look at them. They are moving this way and that."

Of course, what this self-made man was seeing for the first time were the tiny animalcules from the air, until that day unknown to man. The little wiggling forms were microorganisms (yeast, bacteria, and so on) which had settled in the water from the air. But Leeuwenhoek didn't know this.

He reported his observations to the Royal Society in a series of letters over a fifty-year period. The fame of his magic lenses spread and within a short time learned men from many parts of Europe traveled to Holland to witness the new world of subvisible life created by the Dutch merchantman.

After his death, the microscope was used to study microorganisms in more detail, but the similarity between these tiny living organisms and the cells of more complicated organisms was not recognized. It was not until the nineteenth century that the cell theory of life was finally established. In 1838, Matthias Schleiden published his famous monograph on the microscopic anatomy of plants. Among his conclusions, he stated that plants are composed entirely of cells and that these cells are independent living organisms within the larger organism. These ideas were not original. Others before Schleiden had voiced similar opinions, but it was Schleiden and Theodor Schwann, another German biologist, who sold the idea to science.

The story is told that shortly after Schleiden's monograph appeared Schleiden and Schwann met at dinner and discussed their mutual interest. Schwann recognized the similarity in the structure of plant cells described by Schleiden and some animal nerve tissue which he had been studying. The pair went to Schwann's laboratory at the Anatomical Institute and Schleiden confirmed the similarities between his plant cells and the animal cells of Schwann's studies. It is said that the cell theory germinated from these observations. Whether it did or not we leave to the historians. Certainly Schleiden and Schwann publicized the theory, and soon biologists were confirming the idea that all living organisms are composed of one or more cells.

Today we recognize many different types of cells. Some bacteria, for example, appear as short rods, others are round like a ball. In man, the male sperm cells (spermatozoa) with their large, round heads and their long skinny tails resemble a freak polliwog. A nerve cell looks a little like a spider's web. All higher organisms, including man, are composed of cells of various sizes and shapes, each carrying out its own special functions.

Just as the chemist had his unit of chemical structure, the atom, the biologist now had a unit of life, the cell. Understand the cell and you understand the mysterious phenomenon called life. The first step toward this understanding was the study of cell structure. Under a good microscope it is clear that the jellylike protoplasm which is found in every cell is not a homogeneous substance. For example, most cells have a relatively large area of optically dense material which is called the nucleus. The material outside the nucleus is called the cytoplasm. This whole structure is surrounded by a thin membrane, the cell membrane. In addition, some cells, particularly those of plants and some bacteria, have a tough cell wall which surrounds the cell and protects it.

At first, little more than this could be seen of the cell structure. Then in the last half of the nineteenth century a great new field of chemistry—dye chemistry—developed in Germany. Hundreds of dyes were prepared in laboratories of the great German chemists.

Dye chemistry opened up a whole new industry, but it was also of immeasurable aid to the biologist. He soon found that certain parts of the cell had an affinity for certain dyes. With this technique cytologists (biologists who study cells) were able to make various cell structures stand out in contrasting colors. Neither the nucleus nor the cytoplasm were homogeneous substances as had previ-

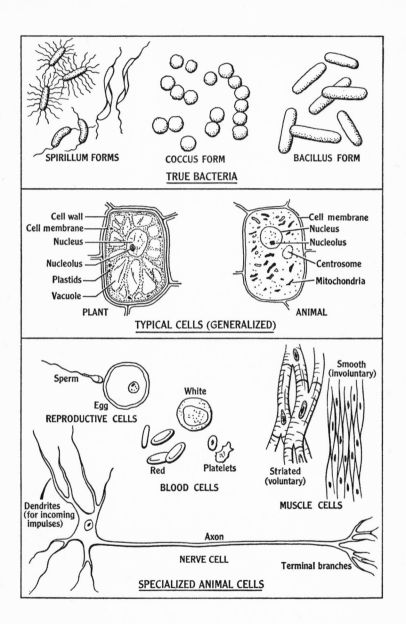

SPIRILLUM FORMS   COCCUS FORM   BACILLUS FORM

TRUE BACTERIA

Cell wall
Cell membrane
Nucleus
Nucleolus
Plastids
Vacuole

PLANT

Cell membrane
Nucleus
Nucleolus
Centrosome
Mitochondria

ANIMAL

TYPICAL CELLS (GENERALIZED)

Sperm
Egg
REPRODUCTIVE CELLS

White
Red   Platelets
BLOOD CELLS

Smooth
(involuntary)

Striated
(voluntary)

MUSCLE CELLS

Dendrites
(for incoming
impulses)

Axon

NERVE CELL   Terminal branches

SPECIALIZED ANIMAL CELLS

ously been supposed. Indeed they seemed to be composed of many tiny granules. But the most powerful microscopes were unable to show the structure of these tiny granules.

Not until the invention of a new kind of microscope—the electron microscope, which uses a stream of electrons instead of light to make objects visible—did our knowledge of cellular architecture advance again. Fantastic magnifications, as high as 100,000 times, are possible with this new tool, and by skillful use of the electron microscope, the structure of the cell as we know it today has emerged.

For example, the thin membrane which surrounds the nucleus appears as a thin, unbroken line under a high powered light microscope. With the electron microscope, it is clear that this membrane is tubular and that there are gaps in it (Diagram B).

The cell membrane, which surrounds the cytoplasm, is porous too, like a finely meshed sieve (C). These holes are too minute to see, but small molecules, of oxygen for example, can easily pass through the tiny openings in this membrane. Larger molecules, such as proteins, are too big to squeeze through. This is a very clever arrangement because it allows the cell to take in small molecules and build them into big ones which become trapped inside. The tiny dots you see in Diagram A, for example, are granules of glycogen, a starchlike carbohydrate which is found in animal cells. The sugar, glucose, has been carried to this liver cell in the blood and then passed through

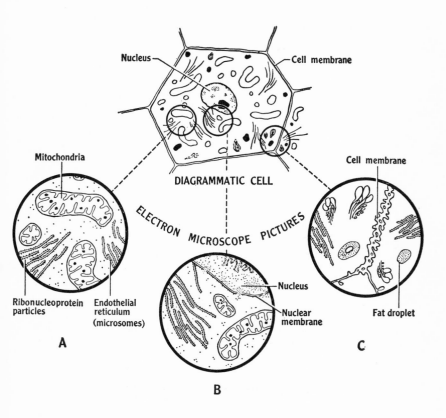

DIAGRAMMATIC CELL

ELECTRON MICROSCOPE PICTURES

Nucleus

Cell membrane

Mitochondria

Ribonucleoprotein particles

Endothelial reticulum (microsomes)

A

Nucleus

Nuclear membrane

B

Cell membrane

Fat droplet

C

the cell membrane into the cytoplasm. Here the cellular machinery goes to work and joins the glucose molecules to form giant glycogen granules which are too big to pass out through the membrane pores. So the glycogen is trapped in the cytoplasm. When the cell needs energy to do some sort of work, it simply breaks the glycogen down to glucose again and then burns up the sugar, a little like a furnace burning coal to produce heat.

The large elliptical structures in Diagrams A and B are called mitochondria. Although they can be seen with a regular microscope, their structure is not clear. The electron micrograph (a picture taken with an electron microscope) (A or B) shows clearly that mitochondria have many finger-like projections with a few dense granules on the inside.

There are, of course, many other cellular structures which the cytologists have studied and described in detail. The *biochemist* wants to know what these structures are made of and how they operate as part of the cell's chemical machinery. Knowing a gasoline engine is composed of cylinders, pistons, valves, and so on doesn't tell us how the engine operates. Similarly, mapping the structure of a cell doesn't tell us how it functions. To understand an engine we must take it apart and to understand a cell we must dismantle it too.

In order to study the individual structures of the cell the cell membrane must first be broken to liberate the cell contents. Several methods can be used to do this. For example, the cells can be ground with sand or homogenized with a special grinding instrument. Some cells can be broken open by exposing them to high frequency sound waves. Next the various components must be separated so that they can be studied independently. This is most conveniently done by a technique called *differential centrifugation.*

A centrifuge is simply a large top which spins at very

high speed. When a test tube containing a suspension of cell particles is placed in the centrifuge the heavier particles are thrown down to the bottom of the tube faster than the lighter ones. By adjusting the speed of the centrifuge properly it is possible to separate the various cellular components. For example, at slow speeds the heavy nuclei are thrown down leaving the lighter particles still suspended in the liquid. This liquid can be poured off and recentrifuged at a higher speed to throw down the mitochondria, and so on. In this way, material representing a single type of structure in the intact cell can be obtained and studied in detail.

Now the biochemist can begin to answer questions such as: What chemical substances are present in the mitochondria and what is their function? What is the chemical role of the nucleus? These are only a few of the many questions we must answer before we can say that we understand how a living cell works. As we shall see, biochemists have made important progress in unraveling the chemical workings of the wondrous cell machine.

Chapter 3

FERMENTATION OPENS
A DOOR

ONE OF MAN'S BEST FRIENDS is a tiny artichoke-colored mold known as *Penicillium chrysogenum*. You may have seen this mold or one of its close relatives on stale bread or spoiling fruit. Perhaps you may have thrown away the contaminated food in disgust. Yet a strain of this mold, which was discovered in a food market in Illinois, is used commercially today to produce the important antibiotic penicillin.

Microorganisms, such as the penicillin mold, are all around us—in the air we breathe, in the water we drink, in the food we eat, in the ground we walk on. In fact, one teaspoonful of ordinary dirt contains about 85 million microorganisms. Most of these little creatures are only about one septillionth (1,000,000,000,000,000,000,000,-000) the size of a human being, but they can band together to do a man-sized job. For example, by the end of World War II the United States pharmaceutical companies were producing 7,000 billion units of penicillin a year—enough to treat seven million patients—with the tiny penicillin mold.

Microorganisms, like all living organisms, are complicated chemical machines. They convert the chemical substances which they obtain from their environment to energy and materials which they need to live. The end products of these reactions are usually excreted by the organism as waste products.

Similar processes occur in all living organisms. Human beings, for example, excrete carbon dioxide, water, and urea as the main waste products from the chemical utilization of carbohydrates, fats, and proteins in the body. The over-all process which is responsible for these conversions is called *metabolism*. Metabolism in microorganisms, however, is often called *fermentation*.

Some of the products of fermentation are harmful to man. For example, the microorganism *Clostridium botulinum* excretes a toxic substance which causes a serious type of food poisoning known as botulism. However, certain fermentation products, such as antibiotics, are beneficial.

Man learned to use fermentation to leaven bread and to produce alcohol long before he understood the process that caused changes to take place in the originating substances. Inscriptions on an ancient clay tablet, thought to have been written in Babylonia about 6000 B. C., are interpreted as depicting the preparation of crude beer. By 4000 B. C., sixteen different kinds of Babylonian beer were produced and constituted an important industry in this ancient civilization. For centuries man was content to observe the bubbling and frothing from which fermentation derives its name (*fervere,* to boil) and to make use of the palatable product. Eventually, however, as with all phenomena, man had to ask, "What is fermentation?"

The ancients explained it as a spontaneous process originating within the fermenting material itself. And indeed it did seem to be spontaneous. Let a sugary solution stand exposed to the air and fermentation soon began of its own accord. There was no way of knowing then that living organisms (yeasts) from the air were causing the fermentations because these tiny organisms were too small to see with the naked eye, and this was before the discovery of the microscope.

Even in the eighteenth century scientists did not suspect that fermentation was caused by a living organism. The great French chemist Antoine Laurent Lavoisier regarded alcoholic fermentation as a purely chemical process. By carefully measuring the quantities of alcohol and carbon dioxide which were formed by the fermentation of sugar, he concluded that these products arose by a chemical splitting of the molecule. In this he was correct, but he was wrong in his explanation of how this occurred. Lavoisier also knew that yeast was required for fermentation of sugar to alcohol, but since he was unable to explain its action he ignored it. Lavoisier's experiments and conclusions are the more remarkable when we realize that his analytical equipment was crude and the chemistry of substances involved in the fermentation process not well understood.

In 1837, the French physicist Charles Cagniard de la Tour published the results of his experiments on fermentation. While he was inspecting some foamy drops of fermenting malt under a powerful microscope he located the tiny yeast globules which Leeuwenhoek had described one hundred and forty years earlier. But here was something that Leeuwenhoek had not described in his voluminous correspondence with the Royal Society. Some of the yeast globules were sprouting buds! Cagniard de la Tour was struck by the similarity between the appearance of these yeast buds and the sprouts of a newly germinated seed.

"These yeasts are alive," he said as he peered at them.

His experiments demonstrated that the spherical yeast particles were indeed capable of reproduction by budding. He believed that the life property of the yeast was responsible for fermentation and that probably as a result of growth, the globules set free carbon dioxide from the sugar solution and changed it into a spirit-containing liquor.

Other scientists confirmed and extended Cagniard de la Tour's observations, but their results were not accepted widely. At this time chemistry was flourishing and the idea that fermentation was caused by living organisms—a biological rather than a chemical process—was unthinkable. For example, Berzelius, the eminent Swedish chemist, stated that microscopic evidence was valueless and that yeast was no more a living organism than precipitate of alumina. It was obvious, however, that the role of yeast in alcoholic fermentation could no longer be ignored and so Berzelius formulated a theory of his own.

It was known that certain chemical reactions (for example, the decomposition of hydrogen peroxide to oxygen and water) were accelerated by the mere presence of certain metals, without the metals themselves undergoing any observable change. To explain this phenomenon, Berzelius introduced a new concept which he called *catalysis* (from the Greek, *Katalysis,* dissolution). A catalyst, by its mere presence and not because of any special reactivity of its own, was able to increase the reactivity of other substances. Thus, metals increased the tendency of hydrogen peroxide to decompose into water and oxygen. Berzelius didn't limit this theory to simple chemicals, but specifically included fermentation as an example of a catalytic process. The yeast, simply by contact with the sugar and not by any biological property of the yeast, was thought to cause fermentation.

The great German organic chemist Justus von Liebig joined Berzelius's attack on the biological nature of fermentation. He denied the role of living organisms in fermentation, but he didn't agree with Berzelius' concept. So he formulated a theory of his own. He believed that putrefaction and fermentation were inseparable. In the case of yeasts their putrefaction caused the sugar to decompose into carbon dioxide and alcohol. Liebig taught his students that no matter how small a sample of yeast globules or rodlike organisms of inoculating material was selected that some of the fermenting liquid was carried along with it. The fermenting liquid caused more fermentation to take place.

These views were widely accepted by the leading chemists of the time, partly because they were reluctant to see fermentation relegated to biology and partly because Berzelius and Liebig were such powerful influences in the scientific world that their disbelief was sufficient to discredit the facts. And so the stage was set—biology against chemistry; experimentation against speculation—for the entrance of the great French scientist Louis Pasteur. Eulogized as "the most perfect man ever to enter the kingdom of science," Pasteur never wavered from his dedication to his chosen profession. His rare genius, his inquiring mind, his insistence on meticulous detail in every experiment, with numerous repetitions of all work to test validity, and his monumental accomplishments, in spite of years of poor health, are well known to anyone who has read about the life of this great scientist. A chemist by training, Pasteur became the world's first bacteriologist, and opened the eyes of mankind to the importance of a new world of living things—the subvisible world of microorganisms.

Pasteur began his scientific career by studying the crystal forms of tartaric acid. Ordinary tartaric acid (Cream of Tartar) crystallized out of wine vats and was collected easily. When a solution of this material was placed in a beam of polarized light the light was rotated to the right and the tartaric acid was said to be optically active. Paratartaric acid, on the other hand, was more difficult to obtain and had no effect on polarized light—it was optically inactive.

Why should these two types of tartaric acid behave differently in polarized light, Pasteur wondered. The greatest chemists of the day could find no other difference between them. Because he was interested in crystal structure Pasteur examined the two forms of tartaric acid under his microscope. He was elated to find that he could tell them apart, but was surprised to find that inactive paratartaric acid was a mixture of two different crystal forms. Laboriously, Pasteur separated the two kinds of crystals into different piles. One of these crystal types was the same as the optically active tartaric acid from the wine vats and, as expected, it rotated polarized light to the right. But the other pile of crystals had the *opposite* effect on polarized light—it rotated it to the left. This was a new type of tartaric acid and Pasteur was the first man to see it.

Pasteur's next experiment was the most exciting of all. He dissolved each pile of crystals in water. One solution rotated polarized light to the right and the other solution rotated it exactly the same amount to the left. Then he mixed the two solutions and the mixture was optically inactive. When he isolated the crystals from this solution he found that he had reformed paratartaric acid.

Pasteur could not contain himself. Running from his laboratory he encountered one of the chemistry assistants in the hall. "I have just made a great discovery," he said. "I am so happy that I am shaking all over and unable to set my eyes again to the polarimeter!" He was then only twenty-seven years old.

It was all clear to him now. Paratartaric acid was a mixture of two crystal types and the reason it had no effect on polarized light was that the effect of one crystal type exactly canceled the effect of the other. The situation is a little bit like a tug of war. As long as both sides (the crystals) pulled equally hard on the rope (the light) nothing happened, but if a few of the pullers (crystals) let go of one side (removal of one crystal type) the rope would start to move toward the other side.

One day Pasteur noticed a mold growing in one of his paratartaric acid solutions causing the solution to ferment and turn cloudy. This was nothing new. Other scientists had observed such occurrences, particularly in hot weather. But unlike other experimenters, Pasteur didn't discard the fermenting solution; instead, he examined it in the polarimeter. Originally, the solution had been optically inactive but now it rotated polarized light slightly to the left. As the fermentation proceeded the light rotated more and more to the left. After the fermentation stopped he crystallized the tartaric acid from the solution and examined the material under a microscope. One of the two crystal forms which had been present originally in the paratartaric acid was now nowhere to be found. It had disappeared completely.

Pasteur concluded, "Two different aspects of this phenomenon require emphasis. As in every true fermentation, there is a substance undergoing chemical alteration and corresponding with this there is the development of a mold-like organism." The mold—a living organism—had metabolized one of the forms of tartaric acid, leaving the other behind untouched.

For Pasteur, the connecting link between alcoholic fermentation and living organisms was amyl alcohol. This alcohol was well known as a product of alcoholic fermentation, and it was optically active. Yet, if made in the laboratory, it was optically inactive like paratartaric acid. To Pasteur nothing but a living organism could cause such preferential treatment of molecules. Liebig assumed that the optical activity of the amyl alcohol produced during fermentation was a consequence of the optical properties of the sugar. Pasteur, on the other hand, held that the amyl alcohol was too remotely related to the sugar to derive any properties from it. Here was another example of the production of an optically active substance by fermentation. Was it not possible that this required a living organism just as in the case of tartaric acid? He believed that each type of fermentation must be related to a particular organism.

This was the hypothesis he set out to test when he began

his fermentation studies in 1855. Shortly after he had become professor of chemistry and Dean of the Faculty of Sciences in the industrial city of Lille, France, the father of one of his students had come to him in desperation. This man was a manufacturer of wines and his wines were going sour. Perhaps Professor Pasteur could help him. Pasteur consented to try.

Although his interest centered on alcoholic fermentation, Pasteur first turned to a study of the less glamorous lactic acid fermentation which was responsible for the souring of milk. This was a wise and possibly strategically calculated choice because one of Liebig's main arguments against the vitalistic concept of fermentation was that no living organisms, such as yeasts, could be found in many fermentations, such as lactic acid fermentation. Pasteur reasoned that if his hypothesis was correct he should be able to find living organisms in the lactic acid mixtures and so disprove one of Liebig's important contentions.

As he carried out his experiment he observed that the deposit of organic matter which settled to the bottom of the vessel during lactic acid fermentation was coated with a gray substance. He carefully removed a sample of the material for microscopic examination. Here before him were tiny cells, pinched in the middle like figure eights— a little like tiny, elongated yeasts. Had he contaminated his material? He thought not, but to be sure he repeated the experiment. The same tiny cells always appeared on the microscope slide.

Now he carried his work a step forward and touched

the tip of a glass rod to the gray matter and then started a fresh medium with the rod. A new fermentation commenced and the little cells were present in large numbers. Moreover, he found that he could continue lactic acid fermentation indefinitely by successive "sowings." These little figure eights were living organisms. Pasteur called them the yeast of lactic acid fermentation. Today we classify them not as yeast but as bacteria, and Pasteur was right in concluding that such organisms cause lactic acid fermentation. Thus, Pasteur disposed of one of the opposition's strong arguments. These lactic acid bacteria had not been seen earlier because they are much smaller than yeasts and were therefore more difficult to observe with the lenses of the day.

Now Pasteur was ready to turn to his real interest, alcoholic fermentation. Liebig had advanced the theory that fermentation was caused by the decomposition of albuminous (nitrogen-containing) material. The albuminous material, in turn, originated from the death and decomposition of the yeasts. There appeared to be some experimental support for this idea, but Pasteur realized that he could disprove it if he could produce fermentation in the absence of albuminous material since this would destroy Liebig's basic postulate.

Pasteur believed that the albuminous material merely served as a source of nitrogen for the growth of yeast. Thus, the essential problem was to grow yeast on a medium containing sugar, as a carbon source, and ammonia, to provide the nitrogen. He found such a medium. It was composed of sugar, ammonium tartrate, inorganic phosphate, some metal salts, and the ashes from some incinerated yeast. Even Liebig would have to admit that there was nothing in this medium which could putrefy. Yet when a small amount of yeast was added to the medium—"about the size of a pin head"—it grew and multiplied, and fermentation occurred. Pasteur had to admit that the yeasts did not grow as well in this medium as they did in grape juice or beer brew, but the amount of alcohol always paralleled the multiplication of the yeasts.

In 1860, Pasteur reported these findings in his now classical paper entitled, "A Note on Alcoholic Fermentation," in which he stated, "Fermentation is a biological process, and it is the subvisible organisms which cause the changes in the fermentation process. What's more, there are different kinds of microbes for each kind of fermentation. I am of the opinion that alcoholic fermentation never occurs without simultaneous organization, development and multiplication of cells, or continued life of the cells already formed. The results expressed in this memoir seem to me to be completely opposed to the opinion of Liebig and Berzelius." Thus the vitalistic theory of fermentation was established—and by a chemist!

Liebig at the age of sixty-six years stood at the head of chemistry, and he refused to accept Pasteur's results. In 1869, he published a long memoir in which, without support of new facts, he weakly refuted Pasteur's conclusions simply by stating that he could not repeat his experiments. (His failure probably was due to the fact that he used a strain of brewer's yeast which has very exacting nutritional requirements and would not grow on Pasteur's simple synthetic medium.)

Pasteur challenged Liebig to submit the matter to a commission of scientists before whom facts would be put to an objective test. He offered to prepare as much yeast as Liebig could reasonably demand from a synthetic medium prepared from materials supplied by Liebig. But Liebig never answered the challenge. Four years later he died and one of the great battles of science ended.

Pasteur had other opponents who carried on after Liebig's death, but it is not our purpose to pursue these controversies. The vitalistic theory of fermentation was on sound experimental footing. The pendulum had swung to the side of biology. Some scientists were satisfied—fermentation was a biological phenomenon and had nothing to do with chemistry. Nothing could have been further from the truth. The conversion of sugar to alcohol and carbon dioxide was obviously a chemical phenomenon no matter how it occurred or what caused it. The most important question remained unanswered: How do living yeast cells carry out this chemical change?

The experiments of both chemists and biologists finally provided the answer to this question. First biologists had to learn how to distinguish one microorganism from another. Countless new organisms, such as protozoa, bacteria, fungi, and yeasts of many kinds, were discovered and classified. Then the members of each group had to be classified, such as round bacteria (cocci), rod-shaped bacteria (bacilli), and so forth.

Chemists were gaining new understandings, too. In fact, a whole new field of chemistry called organic chemistry (the chemistry of carbon-containing compounds) began in 1828 when the twenty-eight-year-old Friedrich Wöhler accidentally produced urea by heating the simple salt ammonium cyanate. This laboratory-made urea was the same urea that man and other mammals excrete in their urine. Previous to Wöhler's discovery, the vitalistic theory of life had reigned supreme. According to this idea, living organisms were endowed with mysterious "vital forces" and "sensitive spirits" which could never be duplicated in the laboratory. The fact that a host of organic substances, such as urea, were produced by living organisms and even the most skilled chemists had not been able to produce these compounds in the test tube seemed to provide evidence for vitalism.

Wöhler's synthesis of urea broke down the barrier between chemistry and biology. "I must tell you," he wrote to his one-time teacher, the great Berzelius, "that I can make urea without calling on my kidneys, and indeed without the aid of any animal, be it man or dog."

Wöhler's discovery opened the door to the laboratory preparation of many organic compounds which previously had only been found in organic matter. The inheritors of his knowledge learned to distinguish one kind of chemical substance from another, how various atoms fit together to form a particular molecule, and how to separate one chemical from another.

The penicillin story illustrates a spectacular application of this discovery. Penicillin was discovered in 1928 by the eminent English bacteriologist Sir Alexander Fleming. Here was a man unplagued by production schedules who was intensely curious about the unexpected. One day as he was working on his studies of bacteria responsible for infections, he observed that one of his *Staphylococcus aureus* culture plates was unlike all the others. It contained a circle of blue-green mold with a bacteria-free ring around it in the center of the plate. Moreover, this mold was not growing in the usual pattern.

Fleming was puzzled. Could the mold be killing the bacteria? Instead of throwing away the contaminated plate, as a less experienced researcher might have done, he removed the interloper and grew it in larger batches. It was a living organism, the mold *Penicillium notatum*. Fleming cultured the mold and tried to extract the chemical with which it had killed the growth of the staphylococcus germs. But this was difficult to do because the chemical was present in such tiny amounts. Finally, he did manage to isolate a very small amount of brownish material. It proved to be a powerful antibiotic capable of killing many kinds of bacteria known to be harmful to man. Fleming named this powerful substance *penicillin* after the mold family which produced it.

Fleming tested his discovery in many ways. For example, he used it to treat severe cases of local skin infection and found that dressings soaked in dilute solutions of penicillin had beneficial effects. In fact, it appeared to be superior to other germicides which were then known. Furthermore, it prevented growth of *Staphylococcus* even when diluted 800 times.

But Fleming could not obtain much of this antibiotic substance because of lack of sufficient assistance. What a few thousand dollars would have done for his work— and for mankind! There were other problems, too. For instance, some of the samples which were isolated were impure and rather toxic to humans. However, he did preserve some of the *Penicillium* mold in a living culture to await the time when it might be studied in greater detail.

Eleven years later that time came. A team of Oxford scientists headed by Sir Howard Florey and Dr. Ernst Chain became interested in finding an antibiotic nontoxic to humans. They selected penicillin as a promising starter. At Florey's request, Fleming sent a culture of *Penicillium notatum* to Oxford. The problem was how to get Fleming's substance out of the mold broth. Dr. Florey's team had been working for months. They had grown molds in earthenware pots and applied one solvent after another to the broth to try to extract the antibiotic. Finally they isolated a small amount of pure penicillin. Could this be the real stuff, pure penicillin? Dr. A. D. Gardner, the bacteriologist on the Oxford team, tested it by dropping minute amounts on growing staphylococcus cultures. The powder stopped the germs in their tracks. The Florey team tested it every possible way—first trying it out on laboratory mice. They obtained satisfactory results—the pure material was not as toxic as Fleming's impure sample had been.

Now Florey was ready to use it on human patients. One of the first subjects was a London policeman who was dying of a blood infection. The penicillin seemed to work miracles. But the supply of the drug was soon exhausted and the policeman died. Within a short time better methods of obtaining the promising drug were devised and many cures followed.

Still the supply was short. World War II was now in progress and had brought into sharp focus the need of better anti-infection agents. Florey believed that penicillin was the key to the problem if only it could be mass produced. But where to turn for this? German bombs were threatening Great Britain's very life line and its industrial capacity was taxed to the limit. Florey decided to turn to the United States for assistance.

Three pharmaceutical companies—Merck, Pfizer, and Squibb—led in assigning personnel and facilities for the project. British manufacturers were also interested in the problem. From the start there was an exchange of scientific information rarely found in industry.

Production problems were gigantic. For one thing, the first penicillin was unstable. Protective devices had to be developed to protect the fermentation culture from invasion by other microbes. And there were other blocks to progress. For instance, the culture was being grown in flasks about the size of milk bottles and the mold which Fleming had discovered was producing only one part of penicillin per million parts of culture medium. Ordinary sea water contains more gold than this. Suddenly, engineers realized that all the milk bottling plants in the country would be inadequate to mass-produce penicillin to meet the need.

To solve the problem, scientists made good use of the knowledge gained by basic research. They screened samples of microorganisms from all parts of the world in an effort to find a mold which would produce larger amounts of this precious drug. Finally, they found what they were looking for—a new strain of penicillin mold, *Penicillium chrysogenum*—growing on a cantaloupe in a Peoria market. This mold thrived in deep tanks and yielded as much as 200 times more penicillin than Fleming's penicillin-producing strain, and it thrived on a corn-steep liquor— a very cheap nutrient. Soon, microbiologists coaxed the mold into producing respectable quantities of penicillin.

This was only half the story. Chemists also contributed vital knowledge. Because of its instability, this prima donna had to be handled with special care or it would turn into a worthless chemical without any antibiotic properties. The first task was to separate it from huge quantities of fermentation medium which was teeming with mold cells. By studying the chemistry of the penicillin molecule, chemists learned how to handle it without

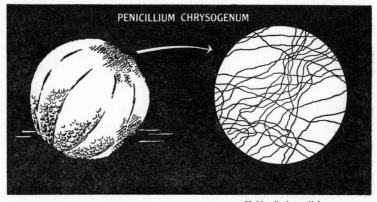

PENICILLIUM CHRYSOGENUM

Cantaloupe with mold

Mold cells (mycelia)
as they appear under the microscope

destroying its biological activity. Then they perfected a technique for picking the chemical needle out of the haystack.

Soon tons of penicillin were being produced. It not only saved thousands of lives of Allied servicemen on the beaches of Normandy and in many of the campaigns which followed D-Day, but since that time has been one of medicine's most valuable infection-fighters.

The penicillin story is a scientific triumph which serves to illustrate how knowledge from several different but related fields of science are required to produce a single "miracle." Penicillin was discovered by a bacteriologist. An organic chemist purified it and determined its chemical structure. It required more bacteriologists, chemists, biochemists, and engineers to put it into the hands of the physician.

Upward of 3,500 different antibiotic substances have been isolated and studied since the discovery of penicillin. Less than twenty are useful in treating disease because of the high toxicity or low potency of the majority of them. But all was not clear sailing even with this select group. First, reports of bacteria resistant to penicillin are almost as old as the drug itself and branded it a narrow-spectrum antibiotic because of its effectiveness against relatively limited varieties of germs. The same problem developed with streptomycin, the second major antibiotic and the first drug to attack the tuberculosis germ directly in the body. The discovery of the broad-spectrum antibiotics (so called because of their effectiveness against a wide range of human, plant, and animal diseases) held hope for a time that these antibiotics would solve the resistance problem by attacking many kinds of germs in potent ways. It was thought that germs with resistant potentialities would have no chance to multiply, or that infections would be cured long before the subtle processes of resistance could be completed. But this didn't happen; resistance to the broad-spectrum drugs began to emerge, slowly but steadily. Then came the present era of combination antibiotics, such as Sigmamycin. Laboratory tests and clinical practice indicate that when certain antibiotics are combined, such as they are in Sigmamycin—the formulated combination of oleanmycin and tetracycline—the combination is not only effective in practically every situation calling for an antibiotic, but is also capable of delivering a two-way knockout punch against some of the stubborn bacteria, known to have become resistant to the older antibiotics. Moreover, combination antibiotics are known to be more effective against disease-causing bacteria than equal amounts of the component drugs when administered separately in equal amounts. Of course, it is too early to say that combination antibiotics are the final answer to this complex problem, but 1956 may be circled as the year of combination antibiotics—a new era in the development of antibiotics.

The appearance of antibiotics gave rise to a huge new pharmaceutical industry. Nonexistent in 1941, it now boasts a capital value measured in millions of dollars. In 1942 and 1943 a little group of drug manufacturers risked their capital to pioneer the production of penicillin, an antibiotic unknown. In those early days production problems were so great, the yield so small, and the need so urgent that for two years the entire output of penicillin was available only to the Armed Services. And they paid twenty dollars for each 100,000 units of the precious stuff. In fact, it was so desperately needed then that it often became necessary to collect the urine from treated patients and re-extract it for use on other war casualties.

Now penicillin and the other antibiotics which followed it are used in the treatment of more than a hundred human ailments. And there is an ever-increasing demand for them in combating a score of livestock ills. Moreover, the modern farmer uses materials which contain antibiotics to condition his soil for better crop yields and to bring his cattle to optimum condition. For example, just a pinch of Terramycin in livestock rations will boost the growth rate of animals and poultry and will increase the number of eggs a well-fed hen will lay. From 1950 to 1953, the use of antibiotics for animal feed supplements reached more than 434,000 pounds at an approximate value of nineteen million dollars.

It took almost twenty years to progress from Fleming's original discovery to the modern, practical, large-scale production of penicillin. And we might still be without the antibiotics if man had not been curious enough to ask, "What is fermentation and what causes it to take place?"

Chapter 4

ENZYMES
THE CORE OF LIFE

HAVE YOU EVER picked up an egg and wondered whether there is a chicken inside its thin shell? If the egg is fertile, it is much more than a mass of egg white and an egg yolk. It is a living organism. If it is not fertile, it is just a bag of chemicals.

How do we know whether a substance is alive or not? Cagniard de la Tour said yeasts were alive because they reproduced. But an oil drop can be made to grow and divide in a way which by casual observation looks very much like the growth and division of certain microorganisms. Yet an oil drop is not a living thing.

Life is difficult to define and even scientists do not agree on what should be called living and what should not. Not all men agreed with Cagniard de la Tour's concept of yeasts as living organisms. Today scientists do agree that yeasts are living organisms, but they do not agree, for example, on whether viruses are alive or not. Biologists often characterize living organisms in terms of responsiveness (reaction to external stimuli such as food or light), metabolism (conversion of food into energy to carry out the function of the cell), and reproduction (perpetuation of the species).

Individually, no one of these properties serves to distinguish in a definitive way the living from the nonliving. A clay pigeon breaks into pieces and falls to the ground when hit with shot from a marksman's gun, yet the pigeon is not alive. However, it has responded to an external stimulus. Or, consider an electric motor: it takes electricity from its environment and converts this electrical energy into work. In a sense, the motor is metabolizing, yet it is not alive.

Arguments of this sort invariably arise whenever one tries to define life. The concept of what is living and what is not is really a learned process. We "know" from our everyday experiences that certain things are alive and others are not. Although no completely satisfactory definition of life has emerged, everyone agrees that, however you define it, life is a remarkable process. Every living thing—plant or animal, large or small—is a highly organized chemical factory. The chemical reactions of the cell are responsible for all the properties which we associate with life—no matter what they may be. These chemical reactions, in turn, are dependent upon a remarkable group of chemical compounds called *enzymes* which inanimate things do not possess.

Enzymes can be extracted from the cells which contain them, giving solid powders or, sometimes, beautiful crystals. These isolated enzymes can carry out the same reactions in the test tube (*in vitro*) as in the cell (*in vivo*). Today we know that enzymes are giant protein molecules which speed up and organize the body's chemical reactions. They are, by definition, the body's catalysts.

The highly organized chemistry of the cell is a little like a modern automobile factory. Metal ore (food) is smelted in huge furnaces (digestion) to make steel (metabolites, the raw materials for the body's chemical reactions). The steel is then fed into machines where the various parts of the cars are made, just as metabolites are converted into the substances the body needs in order to function. Finally, all the parts are assembled to make the finished article, the car, just as the cell components are assembled to produce life.

Of course, this factory requires a number of men and machines to function effectively. Cars could be made without modern mechanization, but it would be impossible to meet the market demand without the highly organized assembly line. This assembly line has to operate as a carefully controlled process so that the proper parts go into the proper places at the right time. Similarly, the body could carry out its reactions without enzymes, but it would be a hopelessly slow and inefficient process. The enzymes are the men and machines of the body's assembly line.

One of the main problems which faces the biochemist is the extraction of enzymes from cells and then the purification of these crude extracts to give a single chemical compound that can be studied in the test tube. First he must obtain fresh tissue which still contains active enzymes. This may require a trip to the slaughter house to get a particular organ from a freshly killed animal. Or the biochemist may grow a fresh batch of bacteria to use as a source of some particular enzyme. Or he may use plant tissues. Whatever the source, the first step is to break open the cells and release the enzymes. Sometimes this is done by grinding them with sand or homogenizing them with a Waring blendor, a duplicate of the household variety. Certain bacterial cells can even be broken open by high frequency sound waves in a machine called a *sonic oscillator*. Then begins the work of separating a particular enzyme from hundreds of other substances which are present in the mixture.

Purification of enzymes is made difficult by their elusive nature. Chemically they are proteins, and because of this special procedures must be used to prevent them from losing their precious biological activity. For example, usually they must be kept cold during the isolation (around 32° F.). It is not at all uncommon to see a biochemist bundled in a fur-lined parka, looking more like an Eskimo than a scientist, working in a giant walk-in refrigerator, very much like the one a butcher uses to store meat. To make the task even more difficult, no two enzymes behave in the same way so that the purification of each new enzyme is usually a painstaking trial and error process. However, the biochemist does have one big helping hand. Enzymes have some specific biological activity. Some break down proteins, others act on fats or carbohydrates, and so on. By following the particular enzyme activity in which he is interested the biochemist can decide whether a particular purification step has been successful or not. Slowly he eliminates the impurities, and as the preparation approaches a pure protein the enzyme may crystallize. To the biochemist this is equivalent to climbing Mt. Everest.

Today about six hundred different enzymes have been isolated and at last count about sixty had been crystallized. As we shall see, a great deal has been learned about the machinery of the cell by studying these isolated enzymes. Today we have more than a century of knowledge to guide our enzyme experiments. This knowledge was hard won. It took the efforts of many researchers who were shown the way by a nineteenth-century German pharmacist and chemist named Kirchhoff.

Kirchhoff became interested in the origin of the sugar produced by seeds during germination or when parboiled with water. A popular view of the time was that the seed absorbed oxygen from the air and combined it with the carbon in the mealy part of the seed to form the sugar and carbon dioxide.

Kirchhoff, dissatisfied with this sketchy explanation, pointed out that grain meal was not a homogeneous substance, but a mixture of several different substances. Certain parts of the meal could form sugar better than others. "One asks himself," he wrote, "which of these components of the meal forms the sugar?"

He had established that when starch was heated with acid, sugar was formed. The amazing thing was that there was as much acid at the end of the experiment as at the beginning—the acid was unchanged during sugar formation. Could part of the meal do the same thing?

To find out, Kirchhoff separated some wheat flour into starch and gluten (a sticky nitrogenous substance) and subjected each of the materials to conditions which favored germination and, therefore, should favor sugar formation. But no sugar was formed. Nor was any sugar formed when the starch or gluten was parboiled.

Next he added some starch to boiling water and after the mixture had cooled slightly, he added some gluten. He set the mixture aside in a warm room and after about ten hours found that the thick paste had become quite thin. He boiled away the water and obtained a slightly yellow syrup which was full of sugar. Thus, gluten had converted parboiled starch to sugar. Kirchhoff was elated.

This was the first experiment to be performed with an isolated enzyme and gluten was the first enzyme preparation. Although Kirchhoff's gluten was a crude mixture of many substances, his investigations were remarkable in that they demonstrated for the first time that a substance could be removed from a living organism and still carry out reactions similar to those which the organism itself carries out.

Kirchhoff's conclusions were correct. Today we know that ungerminated cereals, such as barley, wheat and rye, contain an enzyme called *amylase* which catalyzes the conversion of starch to the sugar, maltose, as required for the nutrition of the plant. Part of the amylase is called free amylase and can be easily extracted from the meal with water. This free amylase undoubtedly was the active enzyme in Kirchhoff's gluten. Part of the amylase is not free, but is bound and cannot be extracted with water. During germination this bound amylase is set free as an active enzyme. This explains why Kirchhoff observed that his preparation from germinating barley was much more active in converting starch into sugar than his preparations from ungerminated wheat flour.

We also know that starch is surrounded by a tough capsule. When this capsule is intact amylase cannot act upon the starch contained inside it. However, if the starch is boiled with water this capsule bursts and liberates the starch molecules. Then the enzyme can go to work. This is why Kirchhoff found it necessary to parboil his preparations before he could observe the formation of sugar.

Not long after Kirchhoff published the results of his researches, other scientists succeeded in obtaining other enzyme preparations which catalyzed the breakdown of specific food substances. For example, an enzyme called *diastase* (meaning, to separate), which also converts starch to sugar, was isolated from germinating barley. This preparation was still a long way from a pure enzyme, but the use of organic solvents, such as alcohol, which were introduced in this work to fractionate crude mixtures, was an important step toward the goal. Within a short time, Theodor Schwann, a German scientist, isolated an enzyme from gastric juice which he called *pepsin*. He found that pepsin broke down proteins in much the same way as diastase acted upon starch.

These and many other enzymes which were isolated in the early days of biochemistry had several features in common: Minute amounts could break down vast quantities of the material on which they worked; furthermore, the reactions catalyzed by these enzymes were extremely rapid. Today these characteristics remain the basic postulates of enzymology, a branch of biochemistry concerned with the study of enzymes.

These properties also describe the characteristic features of fermentation processes. Add a pinch of yeast to a sugar solution and a vigorous fermentation soon begins in which large quantities of sugar are rapidly converted to carbon dioxide and alcohol. Pasteur's experiments had left little doubt that alcoholic fermentation is caused by living yeast cells. The chemical changes catalyzed by isolated enzymes, such as diastase, appeared to be similar in many ways to fermentation. Yet diastase, a dry powder which could be put into a bottle and kept for some time without losing its ability to convert starch to sugar, was no living organism. How could this be explained?

Some scientists believed that the enzymes within the cell were responsible for the results which were observed during the process of fermentation. For some unknown reason, certain enzymes, such as those responsible for alcoholic fermentation, lost their activity when an attempt was made to remove them from the cell.

Even Pasteur admitted this possibility, but "enzymes are always the products of life," he concluded, "and consequently the statement that fermentation is caused by enzymes does not contribute to our understanding of the problem as long as no one has succeeded in separating the fermentation enzyme in active form, free of living cells."

In 1897, the separation of the active fermentation enzyme from yeast cells was accomplished and the door to modern biochemistry thrown open. As in many other important scientific advances, a chance discovery made by Eduard Büchner provided the key to the problem.

Büchner was helping his brother Hans to find a yeast extract of medicinal value which would be nonpoisonous to humans. He knew that the yeast cell was surrounded by a tough membrane. To break this down and so liberate the protoplasm from inside the cell, he ground the yeast with quartz sand. However, he couldn't separate the cell contents from the ground-up mixture of cell membranes, unbroken cells and sand.

On the suggestion of his brother's assistant, Martin Hahn, he combined some *kieselguhr*—a light earthy substance—with yeast and sand, and ground the mixture in a mortar. The mass soon became a dark gray, plasticlike dough. When this dough was wrapped in a cloth and put into a hydraulic press, a liquid seeped out under a pressure which was gradually increased. Within a few hours as much as 500 cubic centimeters of liquid were obtained from 1,000 grams of yeast, or more than half the cell content was pressed out.

Büchner observed that the juice spoiled quickly. He wondered how he could prevent this from taking place. He couldn't use the usual poisonous preservative agents since Hans planned to use the extract for human consumption. So he borrowed from the homemaker's knowledge that a high concentration of sugar will act as a preservative in jam and jelly making and added large amounts of sugar to the yeast extract.

Soon he noticed that movement was occurring in the mixture—bubbles were forming on the surface. Could this be slow fermentation, he wondered. He studied the mixture very carefully and to his elation found that the sugar was converted to alcohol and carbon dioxide. Fermentation had indeed taken place and *in the absence of living cells.*

What an amazing discovery, yet it was only the start of a series of experiments carried out by Büchner. His researches led him to conclude, "The production of alcoholic fermentation does not require so complicated an apparatus as the yeast cell, and the fermentation power of the yeast enables the organisms to convert substances which it obtains from its environment into other substances which it needs to live." Büchner named his enzyme preparation *zymase*.

Not all scientists accepted Büchner's results, although his discovery did create a furor in scientific circles. One of the most serious criticisms of his work was directed to the presence of living organisms in the zymase. Sceptics suggested, "Perhaps these organisms and not the zymase are responsible for fermentation."

Büchner admitted the presence of these organisms, but showed that antiseptics which killed them could be added to the zymase without destroying its capacity to ferment sugar. For his opponents, Büchner usually had an experimental answer. However, as late as 1927, a few scientists were still trying to disprove the concept of cell-less fermentation. But by that time, the advances of the twentieth century were so great that Büchner's work was thoroughly confirmed.

In 1907, he was awarded the Nobel Prize in chemistry "for his biochemical researches and his discovery of cell-less fermentation." A chance discovery? Perhaps, but as Pasteur so perfectly stated, "In the field of observation, chance favors the trained mind."

Through the door to modern biochemistry which Büchner opened have passed hundreds of biochemists, and through their combined efforts much has been learned about the role of enzymes in living cells. We know, for example, that zymase is not a single enzyme but a mixture of twelve different enzymes. Each of these enzymes has been isolated and purified. In addition, each of the steps catalyzed by these enzymes has been studied in detail until now it is possible to reconstruct alcoholic fermentation by mixing purified enzymes from the biochemist's deep freeze.

Of course, alcoholic fermentation is only one of the cellular processes which is dependent upon enzymes. In fact, almost every one of the hundreds of chemical reactions which go on in *every* living cell is catalyzed by some specific enzyme. One of the most important contributions to our understanding of living organisms has come from biochemical studies on isolated enzymes. As a result of these experiments we know how carbohydrates, such as glucose, are converted to carbon dioxide and water to furnish energy for important body functions. Muscle contraction, for example, or reading this page, utilizes this enzyme-liberated energy. The enzymes which break down fat to yield energy as well as most of those which build up the fat stores from carbohydrates have been purified by biochemists.

Isolated enzymes or groups of enzymes have found some practical uses, too. For example, meat tenderizers —a recent addition to the home seasoning shelf—are nothing more than a crude preparation of an enzyme from the tropical fruit, papaya. This enzyme, *papain,* partially digests the meat protein, much as pepsin digests proteins in the stomach. This process tenderizes the coarser, tough cuts of meat.

The textile industry is another field which has benefited from the hard-working enzymes. The basic steps in producing fabrics from raw fibers consist in first converting fiber into threads, weaving them into fabrics, then finishing the raw material by suitable bleaching, dyeing, patterning, and so forth. The warp threads have to be strengthened or sized before they can be woven. In cotton and rayon weaving, this is usually accomplished with solutions of modified starch. Raw starches are seldom used today; common practice now is to liquefy starch suspensions with amylases for the production of suitable sizing materials.

Amylases and proteases are quite widely used in the desizing of woven materials before dyeing and bleaching. Bacterial protease preparations are also used for partially degumming silk so as to free the raw fiber from part of its naturally accompanying sericin before it is converted into yarn. Similarly, bacterial proteases are often used for degumming finished fabrics and are especially useful in the treatment of mixed fabrics.

Medicine, too, has profited. *Streptodornase,* an enzyme preparation from the *Streptococcus* bacteria, has been used successfully to clean out infected wounds and promote their healing. Other enzymes have been used in many other ways in medicine and it seems possible that enzymes will play an even more important role as a disease-fighter in the future.

Yet with all this progress, there remain many unanswered, basic questions about enzyme characteristics and behavior. For instance, we don't yet know the exact chemical structure of a single enzyme. Nor do we know *how* enzymes exert their catalytic effect. Why are they proteins? Why not carbohydrates? Why are enzymes such large molecules? and so on.

There seems to be almost no limit to the things enzymes can do. At times, they seem to be almost magical, but this is mainly because we don't really understand them. Some day scientists will know all about the enzyme reactions which occur in living organisms, their relationship to one another, their function, and how they are controlled. When that time comes perhaps we shall understand life itself.

Chapter 5

CHEMISTRY OF PROTEINS

ONE DAY in the mid-'twenties Dr. James B. Sumner rushed to the telephone in his laboratory and placed a call to his wife. "I have just crystallized the first enzyme," he told her excitedly.

This was no chance discovery. Sumner believed that enzymes were proteins, and reasoned that if this were true he should be able to purify them by known techniques of protein chemistry. His studies on the enzyme urease, which led to the first crystalline enzyme, represented nine years of hard work and hundreds of experiments.

Like many other scientists, Sumner was a dedicated man. In his Nobel Prize address he said: "I wish to tell you . . . why I decided in 1917 to attempt to isolate an enzyme. At the time I had little time for research, not much apparatus, research money or assistance. I desired to accomplish something of real importance. In other words, I decided to take a 'long shot.' A number of persons advised me that my attempt to isolate an enzyme was foolish, but this advice made me feel all the more certain that, if successful, the quest would be worth while."

Worth while it certainly was. In fact, Sumner's crystallization of urease was a biochemical milestone. The chemical nature of at least one enzyme was at last on solid ground. It was no longer necessary to regard enzymes as mysterious substances of unknown nature—they were definite chemical compounds which the chemist could isolate and study. This provided a new stimulus for biochemists. Perhaps experiments would reveal other enzymes to be proteins too.

Today more than six hundred enzymes have been purified and all of them are proteins. But not all proteins are enzymes. For example, hair and nails are rich in the structural protein *keratin;* red blood cells are packed with a special respiratory protein called *hemoglobin*. However, all proteins have certain chemical features in common, regardless of their specialized biological function.

One of the most striking characteristics of proteins is their size. Thousands, and in some cases millions, of atoms are hooked together to form the protein molecule. And yet the largest protein molecule is too small to be seen with a microscope. By the standards of the world around us, proteins are small, but in the cellular world they are giants, and the biochemist calls them *macromolecules.*

Amino acids (containing ten to twenty-seven atoms) are the basic building blocks of proteins. These relatively simple molecules are linked together like a string of beads to form the protein. Sometimes, these chains of amino acids are stretched out to form fibrous proteins, such as keratin, or they may be coiled into a ball, as in hemoglobin. These differences in shape are partly responsible for the variation in properties from one protein to another. The biochemist utilizes these differences to separate a mixture of proteins into pure compounds. However, the isolation of a pure enzyme is a tedious and difficult job which requires special techniques, a lot of patience, and a little luck. In fact, when the difficulty of the task is considered, even with modern methods, it is not surprising that almost a century elapsed between the isolation of the first solid enzyme powder (diastase) and the crystallization of the first pure enzyme (urease).

To set the stage for Sumner's important discovery, let us retrace a little of the uphill story of proteins. In the nineteenth century, Gerardus Mulder, a Dutch chemist, recognized a new class of biological substances which he named *protein* (from Greek *prōteios,* holding first place). Mulder found that proteins had several unique properties which distinguished them from other biological materials, such as fat and carbohydrate. They contained nitrogen, for example, and could be coagulated easily by heat or strong acid. He found proteins in all plant or animal tissues that he examined. This led him to conclude that they were essential for life. He also believed that proteins from both animal and plant sources were identical and differed only in their molecular arrangements. To use an analogy, string is string, but it can assume many shapes. It can be rolled into a tight ball, stretched out straight or loosely coiled. Whatever is done with it, it retains its identity as string.

As more refined methods of analysis were introduced, scientists learned that these proteins were not identical. The work of Ritthausen in Germany and the later experiments of Thomas Burr Osborne, a distinguished biochemist in the United States, showed that protein preparations which had been studied were far from pure substances. Ritthausen found that the plant fibrins, for example, consisted of at least two different proteins which he called *legumin* and *conglutin*. Similarly, the alcohol-soluble gliadin obtained from wheat was shown to be a mixture of several proteins. Protein preparations from other sources, both plant and animal, also proved to be mixtures rather than pure substances.

First, Osborne studied the oat kernel and followed this with experiments on a wide range of plant seeds and the preparation of pure specimens of their proteins. In every case, each different seed yielded several different proteins. The only criterion then available to determine protein purity was analysis of the elemental composition of each substance. Osborne knew this was inadequate, but what would be better, he asked. He turned to the analysis of amino acids in the proteins and thus laid the foundation not only for later nutritional studies but also for the protein structure studies.

Pioneer protein chemists, such as Osborne, established that all proteins could be distinguished from other biological materials by relatively simple chemical tests. For example, certain chemicals produced colored solutions when they reacted with proteins. Furthermore, proteolytic enzymes (enzymes which break down proteins), such as pepsin, were specific for proteins, that is, they would catalyze the breakdown of proteins but not carbohydrates or fats.

At this time the chemical nature of enzymes was still uncertain, but there was evidence that they were proteins. For example, they gave colored solutions with the protein reagents, and they were digested by proteolytic enzymes. In addition, the purification procedures which worked for proteins also seemed to work for enzymes. In fact, all the properties which enzymes possessed suggested that they were indeed proteins, but positive proof was lacking because no one had succeeded in obtaining an enzyme of sufficient purity to say for sure that the protein, and not some other material of unknown nature, was responsible for the activity of the preparation. We can use a colored block analogy to illustrate this point. Imagine that we have a pile of red blocks except for a few blue strays which remain in spite of all efforts to get rid of them. The pile of blocks has a certain enzymatic activity and, since most of the blocks are red, it seems logical to assign enzyme activity to them. However, because enzymes are so reactive, it is possible that the enzyme activity is actually due to the few blue blocks which are regarded as an impurity.

This was the state of affairs when James Sumner began his research on urease in 1917. Sumner was a Harvard graduate, one-time knitting factory worker and chemistry teacher. However, he didn't remain in these fields for long, but returned to Harvard, this time to the Medical School, where he studied under the famed Otto Folin, and received his doctor's degree in biochemistry in 1914. Shortly afterward, he accepted an appointment at Cornell University where he remained as professor of biochemistry until his death in 1955.

Sumner was one of the biochemists who believed that enzymes were proteins and he was determined to prove it. He chose to study urease because cheap sources of the starting material were available in various plant and animal tissues which contained the enzyme. Furthermore, the biological activity of urease was easy to follow simply by measuring the amount of urea which it broke down in a given period of time. Sumner selected the jack bean as his source material because he could grow the bean himself at very little cost and because it was unusually rich in urease. He set out to isolate the enzyme in pure form and to describe it chemically.

By measuring the amount of urea broken down in a given period of time, Sumner was able not only to follow urease activity, but also to determine whether a particular operation had improved the purity of the enzyme. (The principle involved here is true for any enzyme—if you hope to purify it, you must have some way to follow its activity.)

In the beginning, Sumner mixed jack bean meal with water and obtained a thin, brownish soup. But where was the enzyme? Was it in the watery extract or in the bean grinds? To find out, Sumner added a small amount of urea to each. The extract commenced almost at once to tear apart urea into carbon dioxide and ammonia. Nothing happened with the insoluble bean grinds. So the enzyme was in the extract! Now began the tedious task of eliminating the impurities from the solution and concentrating the enzyme. Time after time Sumner had to test both the substances discarded from the solution and the solution remaining behind for enzymatic activity.

Along the way in his many experiments he learned that Folin used 30 per cent alcohol extracts of bean meal as a source of urease for analytical purposes, so he switched to this with good results. The solvent dissolved most of the urease, yet failed to dissolve a considerable quantity of other proteins. So by using the 30 per cent solutions he increased the purification of his material. The alcoholic extracts were filtered quickly, leaving on the filter the undissolved material. The one disadvantage of the alcohol was that it slowly inactivated the urease. To prevent this Sumner kept the alcoholic extracts at low temperatures. At this time he had no refrigeration in the laboratory so he placed the cylinders of 30 per cent alcohol extracts on window ledges and hoped for cold weather. Precipitates obtained from these cold extracts had high urease activity.

These new solutions were a great improvement over those first water extracts, yet he was not entirely satisfied. So he substituted dilute acetone for the alcohol and chilled the mixture overnight in the new icebox which the laboratory now boasted. Perhaps this departure would improve the method of purification. The next morning he examined the solution under a microscope. There before him were many tiny, colorless, octahedral-shaped crystals—a shape he hadn't noticed in any of his previous work. "I centrifuged off some of the crystals and observed that they dissolved readily in water. I then tested the water solution. It gave tests for protein and possessed a very high urease activity. I then telephoned my wife, 'I have crystallized the first enzyme.' "

Sumner's crystallization of urease was a tremendous achievement, but it did not establish with certainty that the activity was due to the protein itself. Sumner gave several reasons why he thought that the protein and the enzyme were identical. In the first place, the activity of the crystalline material was very high—it would decompose its own weight in 1.4 seconds. Furthermore, it gave all the protein color tests, but no tests for other material

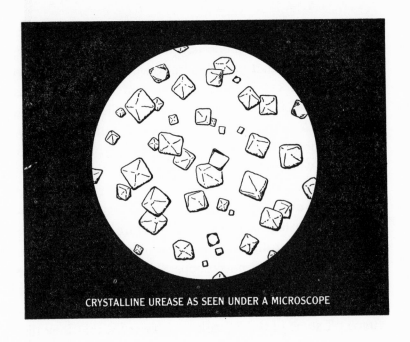

CRYSTALLINE UREASE AS SEEN UNDER A MICROSCOPE

which ordinarily contaminate protein preparations. It was coagulated by heat, precipitated by salt, and so on. In fact, everything he tried indicated that the substance was a protein, and there was no evidence to the contrary. However, Sumner had no idea how pure his substance was because no reliable criteria of purity had yet been developed and crystallinity by itself was no assurance that the substance was pure.

Sumner's discovery stimulated other biochemists to attempt the crystallization of enzymes. One of the most notably successful of these pioneers was John Howard

Northrop, at the Rockefeller Institute, who believed that a great scientific advance had been made. Sumner's results encouraged him to undertake once again a study of the enzyme pepsin with the idea of crystallizing it by using modern methods of protein chemistry. In 1930, he isolated crystalline pepsin from a commerical preparation of this enzyme. Soon after, Kunitz and others in Northrop's laboratory isolated and crystallized several enzymes, such as trypsin and chymotrypsin. All were proteins.

Northrop believed that all enzymes were probably proteins, although he admitted that crystallization of a few protein enzymes did not prove this point. He also pointed out that crystallinity was no assurance of homogeneity although it usually indicated a considerable degree of purity. He spent a lot of time developing methods for establishing the purity of his preparations.

From Northrop's time on, the list of crystalline enzymes grew until by 1956 it contained more than sixty different enzymes. Each year new enzymes are crystallized, and all of them so far have the properties of proteins.

In 1946, Sumner and Northrop were named Nobel Prize winners in chemistry for their contributions to enzyme chemistry. How hard these scientists had labored to prove their point! And in so doing, they provided the stimulus which led to our modern methods for establishing protein purity.

Today there are perhaps a half dozen methods used in determining protein purity. One of the most frequently employed techniques is based on the principle that *in solution* heavy objects fall faster than light ones under the influence of gravity. Theoretically, this should make it possible to distinguish between molecules of different weights. However, even with macromolecules, such as proteins, the force of gravity is not strong enough to allow practical measurements of this kind to be made.

To circumvent this difficulty, a Swedish physical chemist named Theodor Svedberg developed an ingenious machine, the *ultracentrifuge,* which was capable of reaching much higher speeds than conventional centrifuges. The rotor in the ultracentrifuge spins around like a top at

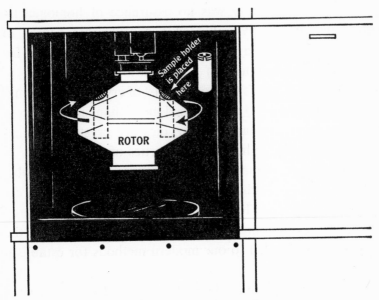

ROTOR OF AN ANALYTICAL ULTRACENTRIFUGE

speeds as high as 60,000 revolutions a minute and develops a centrifugal force 260,000 times as great as gravity. Using a complicated optical system, photographs can be obtained which represent the movement of molecules at this high centrifugal field. By inspecting the photographs the biochemist can often decide whether his preparation is a single protein or a mixture.

However, the ultracentrifuge didn't distinguish between two proteins of similar shape and molecular weight. Therefore, another check for purity based on a different property was needed. It was known that protein molecules carry both positive and negative electrical charges. The distribution of these charges, which was usually different for different proteins, could be altered by changing the acidity (or pH as the biochemist calls it) of the protein solution. Theoretically, if two proteins carrying different charges were placed in an electrical field, they should move at different rates depending upon their charge. Furthermore, proteins with unlike net charges, that is positive or negative, should move in opposite directions.

This phenomenon is known as *electrophoresis* and it was exploited by the Swedish biochemist Arne Tiselius who, in 1933, developed a machine which made it possible to measure movement of protein molecules in an electric field. He was awarded a Nobel Prize for this work.

Using powerful tools, such as ultracentrifugation and electrophoresis, biochemists have established the homogeneity of many crystalline enzymes. There is no longer any doubt that these protein molecules actually carry the enzymatic activity. And so an old biochemical question has been answered. But we still do not understand enzymes completely. For example, why do some proteins have catalytic activity while others do not? In order to answer this question we must determine the structure of the protein in question; we must know how each atom is placed in the protein molecule. Today some exciting progress toward this goal is being made.

You will remember that proteins are composed of amino acid building blocks linked together in chains. Once a pure protein has been obtained the first problem is to find out how many different kinds of amino acids are present in the protein and how much of each kind. Fifteen years ago this took months to accomplish and even then the results weren't too reliable. Even five years ago it took more than a week to perform amino acid analysis. Now, thanks to an ingenious device developed by Moore and Stein at the Rockefeller Institute for Medical Research, this laborious task can be completed automatically in twelve hours.

Once the amino acid composition is known the next step in determining protein structure is to find the sequence of amino acids in the protein chain. To see how the biochemist attacks this problem, let us follow the work that was done to determine the structure of the enzyme *ribonuclease*.

Ribonuclease was discovered in 1920 and found to

catalyze the breakdown of important cellular material called *ribonucleic acid* (see Chapter 13). In 1939, Kunitz crystallized the enzyme and in the early 1950's preparations of suitable purity for structural studies were obtained by Moore and Stein's group. Analysis of the protein showed that it contains 126 amino acids arranged in a single chain. There are 17 different kinds of amino acids —15 aspartic acids, 12 glutamic acids, 3 glycines, and so on. Of course, the problem was to find the order of the amino acids in the chain.

Perhaps a crude analogy will help to visualize this. Imagine that each amino acid is represented by a colored block and each color represents a different kind of amino acid—red for aspartic acid, blue for glutamic acid, and so on. Ribonuclease will be represented by a string of 126 blocks since there are 126 amino acids in this protein. There are 17 different kinds of amino acids so we will need 17 different colors for our blocks. This ribonuclease model will have 15 red blocks for aspartic acid and 12 blue ones for glutamic acid, and so on, arranged in definite places in the protein chain. In other words, the nuclease molecule contains a definite number of each different amino acid arranged in a specific sequence in the chain of 126 building blocks.

Now we must find the color sequence: Is it red-blue-blue-green or blue-red-blue-green? et cetera. This is a particularly hard task because the biochemist can't pick up a protein chain and look at the color sequence as we would with our chain of blocks. He has to use chemical methods to find the amino acid sequence. And as the chain lengthens, so does the task.

Ribonuclease is a fairly small molecule as proteins go, and yet it is much too big to proceed down the chain in an orderly fashion, chemically breaking off one amino acid at a time, to determine the sequence. Instead, the protein must first be broken down into smaller chains of amino acids called *peptides.* The Rockefeller workers used proteolytic enzymes for this purpose. From the results of other scientists, they knew that trypsin would break an amino acid chain whenever the amino acid lysine or arginine occurred. And there were 10 lysines and 4 arginines in ribonuclease. They treated ribonuclease with trypsin and laboriously isolated the products. Sure enough, there were the expected 13 peptides.

They repeated the procedure with another enzyme, *chymotrypsin,* which usually splits protein chains whenever the amino acids phenylalanine or tyrosine occur. Twenty additional peptides were eventually isolated and none of them had more than 8 amino acids. The sequence of amino acids in a peptide of this size could be determined.

Year after year, they plugged away at this problem by isolating pieces of the ribonuclease molecule and determining the amino acid sequence in these small pieces. Finally, after five years they fitted the giant jigsaw puzzle together. The year 1958 will go down in biochemical history as the time when the amino acid sequence of an enzyme was worked out for the first time.

Such information should help us to understand the chemical reasons for the biological action of ribonuclease. But Moore and Stein point out that we will have to know more than the amino acid sequence of a single enzyme before we can hope to understand enzymes. We will have to obtain similar information for many enzymes, and then we will have to determine how these amino acid chains fold up in the native protein molecules. Then perhaps we can answer such questions as: Why is one protein an enzyme, another a hormone and still another an antibody?

Tomorrow's research will answer today's perplexities, but thanks to our enzyme pioneers, at least we know what enzymes are and what they do.

Chapter 6

THE LOCK AND KEY

EVERYONE KNOWS that you can't fit a square peg into a round hole. Enzymes are choosey, too. They won't catalyze reactions with just any chemical substance that comes along. Special geometric and chemical requirements must be met before an enzyme will act. This selection is called *enzyme specificity*. For example, urease will act only on urea. In some way, which we don't completely understand, the urea molecule fits onto the urease molecule and breaks down to ammonia and carbon dioxide which is released from the protein surface. Then the process is repeated over and over again. Each enzyme molecule (urease) breaks down many urea molecules.

The concept of enzyme specificity was a result of the brilliant work of Nobel Laureate Emil Fischer. He began his career in Germany in the 1870's when organic chemistry was in full bloom. New compounds were being synthesized every day in Germany, England and France. Emil worked with his brother Otto for a time, studying the chemistry of rosaniline dyes. His real ambition, however, was to work on the chemistry of materials intimately connected with life phenomena so he soon turned his attention to the chemistry of the poorly understood carbohydrates.

His first experiments had to do with the synthesis of sugar. He managed to obtain a syrupy mixture, but it took four years to isolate the sugar. That he could accomplish it then was due to the help of a new reagent, phenylhydrazine, which he had discovered shortly after he was awarded his doctor's degree at Strasbourg. Fischer found that phenylhydrazine was of great value because it combined with simple sugars, such as fructose or glucose, to form compounds which were easy to crystallize. These new derivatives of the sugars could be easily purified and identified, thus assisting in working out the detailed structure of various sugars.

In 1864, Fischer undertook the study of the action of yeast extracts on some of the sugar derivatives he had prepared. He found that even simple carbohydrates exist in several forms and are closely related. For example, there are fifteen different kinds of sugar molecules which are close chemical relatives of glucose. These various sugars have the same chemical groups—they are isomers—but the spacial arrangement of these groups is different in each isomer.

We can visualize this kind of isomerism by looking at one of our hands. If we could switch the position of any two fingers, such as the middle and little fingers, we would still have a hand composed of five fingers, but its appearance certainly would be different with the tall middle finger jutting up at the end of the hand and the little finger indenting the index and ring fingers. Actually, all that would be different would be the spacial arrangement of the five fingers. In the chemical world such isomers have very similar chemical properties although differences do exist. The sugars glucose and mannose are isomers, but the chemist has no trouble in separating them. Fischer found that enzymes also can distinguish isomers of this special type, and usually each isomer is acted upon by a separate enzyme.

Enzymes can even beat the chemist at his own game. When isomers are mirror images of one another, such as the right and left hand, they become chemically identical. In fact, the only difference between them is that one isomer rotates polarized light to the left and the other isomer rotates light in the same amount to the right. Yet enzymes with their special characteristics can detect this subtle difference and will usually only catalyze a reaction with one of the mirror-image isomers. When the chemist carries out the same reaction in the test tube without the aid of enzymes, both isomers usually react.

At first this seems surprising. However, if we assume that isomers attach to the surface of the enzyme through the same chemical group—and this is a reasonable assumption—then this process is not difficult to understand. Now using the hand analogy again, let us say that the left hand represents one isomer and the right hand another isomer. Let us also assume that your hand has to attach to the enzyme surface (such as this page) through the palm. You will see that no matter how your right hand is turned it won't coincide with the left one as long as both palms are down—either the thumbs or the other fingers point in opposite directions.

If the specificity of the enzyme requires that the compound attaches to its surface with the "thumb" to the right and the "fingers" up in order to react, then you will see that only the "left-hand isomer" can react—no matter how you turn your right hand, you cannot satisfy the conditions for reaction (palm down, thumb right and fingers up).

Fischer recognized this difference between the two isomers and realized that if one of them fitted exactly in one type of enzyme molecule, probably the other would not fit. Or if it did fit into the space, it would not be able to react. Thus, he concluded that each isomer requires its own enzyme.

To explain the specificity between the substrate (a compound which reacts on an enzyme surface) and the enzyme Fischer used the famous lock and key analogy. The enzyme is like the lock of a door and the substrate the key which opens the lock. For a molecule to fit the enzyme surface, it must have the right shape, just as the key must be shaped to fit the particular lock. Only one key with its special shape will open a particular lock. Similarly, only one compound or group of compounds will react with a specific enzyme. A closely related chemical compound might fit onto the enzyme surface and still be unable to react, just as several keys might fit into a lock, but only the one with the correct shape and properties can open it.

This is the basis of enzyme specificity. Some enzymes, such as urease, are absolutely specific—that is, they have only one substrate. Others, such as pepsin, are group specific and will act on a number of substances. Enzyme specificity is, of course, of vital importance to the living organism. It makes sure that the right chemicals undergo the right reactions at the right time. This characteristic is like the assembly line of the automobile factory where each machine does its specific job and then passes on its product part to the next machine where another special job is completed.

The enzymatic reactions of all living organisms are very much alike in many ways. Many of the same enzymes which carry out the metabolic reactions of bacteria are also present in plants and animals. Because of this biochemical unity, it has been possible to study the enzymatic reactions of relatively simple organisms, such as bacteria, to gain valuable information about more complicated organisms, such as man. However, important differences do exist at the biochemical level. For example, *Streptococcus hemolyticus,* the bacterium which causes such diseases as strep throat and childbed fever, has enzyme systems which require folic acid to function normally. Man also requires folic acid, but he must obtain it from his diet because he lacks certain enzymes which are needed to make this vitamin from other dietary substances. *Streptococcus hemolyticus,* on the other hand, doesn't need dietary folic acid because it has the enzymes which can do their own manufacturing job. The effectiveness of the sulfa drugs in fighting strep infections is based on biochemical differences between man and microorganisms.

Before 1935, without adequate drugs, there wasn't much a physician could do for patients suffering from strep infections except to order good nursing and hope for the best. For many years pharmacologists had searched in vain for antistreptococcal drugs which would be active in the blood stream. They screened a great many compounds without any success. Then in the 'thirties, after testing more than a thousand dyes, Domagk, a German doctor, discovered that one of the substances gave the desired effect. The compound was nicknamed Prontosil and its discovery marked a new era in medicine.

It was certainly a wonder drug. It passed preliminary tests with mice and proved to be harmless to them. The first human patient to be treated with it was Domagk's young daughter who was desperately ill with streptococcal blood poisoning. She recovered. This was the first of many spectacular successes with the use of Prontosil. At last the physician had an invaluable aid in the treatment of a host of strep infections.

Although the drug gave dramatic results in cases of animal and human strep infections, it had no effect on these bacteria in the test tube. The simplest explanation was that Prontosil was converted to some other compound in the body. The first clue as to the nature of the substance came from the work of Tréfouel and his co-workers at the Pasteur Institute in Paris. They treated Prontosil with a reducing agent and found that one of the products—sulfanilamide—inhibited bacterial growth equally well in the test tube or in the body. Moreover, a similar conversion occurred in the body, and sulfanilamide, not Prontosil itself, was the active antibacterial agent. This important discovery not only gave the physician a powerful new weapon in the treatment of certain diseases, but also stimulated scientific interest in the mechanism of sulfanilamide action in the body.

One of the scientists who became interested in this problem was the English biochemist D. D. Woods. At the time he began his experiments, it was well established that sulfanilamide did not kill bacteria, but rather it *inhibited their growth* so that the body's natural defenses could overpower them. Woods reasoned that sulfanilamide might be preventing the action of some enzyme which played a vital role in bacterial growth. Perhaps, he thought, sulfanilamide was a key which fitted into the enzyme lock without being able to open it. If this were true it would prevent the correct key from entering the lock and opening it. In other words, the enzyme couldn't function normally.

To test this hypothesis, Woods prepared a simple culture medium (some phosphate, the amino acid glutamine, glucose, and some well-known growth factors) on which *Streptococcus hemolyticus* grew well. Then he added enough sulfanilamide to inhibit bacterial growth for at least five days. Now the problem was to find a substance which would overcome this growth inhibition. Woods added various known growth factors, but exhausted the list without success.

"Perhaps there are some growth factors we don't yet know about," he mused. So he decided to study the effect of cell extracts for a possible answer. Yeast had been a good source of growth factors in the past. Why not try it here? He prepared a yeast extract and added it to the growth-inhibited streptococcus cultures. The bacteria began to grow again!

Woods worked up the yeast extract and managed to isolate a solid material which had the proper biological activity; it reversed sulfanilamide inhibition. But he had very little material and what he had was not completely pure. Because of its impurities, he couldn't determine the full chemical structure of the substance, although he did detect the presence of certain chemical groupings. He found that many of the chemical properties of this yeast factor were very much like those of sulfanilamide.

He also observed that if the concentration of sulfanilamide was increased it became necessary to increase the concentration of the yeast factor in order to reverse the inhibition of growth. The sulfanilamide and the growth factor seemed to be competing with each other. Now he began to fit the pieces of the puzzle together.

He knew that in most cases competitive inhibition of an enzyme is caused by compounds whose structure is very similar to that of the natural substrate. "If this principle holds true," Woods reasoned to his colleagues, "the substance which reverses inhibition should be closely related to sulfanilamide."

With information about the structure of the growth factor and the known chemical structure of sulfanilamide, he made a calculated guess and hit the jackpot. He added some para amino benzoic acid (PABA)—a close chemical relative of sulfanilamide—to the inhibited cultures of *Streptococcus hemolyticus*. Sure enough, the inhibition was reversed and the cultures began to grow. He also found that the effect of sulfanilamide on certain other bacteria was reversed by PABA.

He concluded, "Although the similarity in many different properties provides strong circumstantial evidence for identity, it must be remembered that para amino benzoic acid has not yet been obtained from yeast and the final proof lies in an actual isolation."

Finally, PABA was isolated not only from yeast and Streptococcus, but also from other sulfanilamide-sensitive bacteria. It was clear that PABA was required for normal growth in many microorganisms. Somehow sulfanilamide interfered with the normal utilization of PABA. But how did this take place?

The last link in the chain of evidence came with the discovery of a new vitamin, folic acid. As we have seen, all organisms require this vitamin to carry out their normal metabolic reactions. However, during evolutionary changes which occurred over the ages, certain organisms, including man, lost their ability to make folic acid and therefore require a dietary supply of this vitamin. Other organisms, such as *Streptococcus hemolyticus,* can make their own folic acid from PABA and other normal dietary constituents.

The action of sulfanilamide can now be explained in terms of enzyme specificity and species differences. Let's go back to the lock and key analogy once again. The conversion of PABA to folic acid is an enzymatic process and the normal key which fits and opens the enzyme lock is PABA. PABA is then converted to folic acid and the organism grows normally. Sulfanilamide is so similar to PABA that it also fits into the space on the enzyme surface normally occupied by the PABA, and, if enough sulfanilamide is present, essentially all the PABA is pushed off the enzyme. Although these two compounds are similar, they are not identical, and the enzyme can distinguish between them. Sulfanilamide fits into the keyhole, but it can't turn the lock. No folic acid is formed and the bacteria can't grow. Since man gets his folic acid in his diet, sulfanilamide has no effect on his metabolic reactions.

The solution of the action of sulfanilamide also had

COMPETITIVE INHIBITION

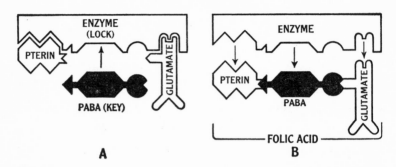

A

B

Folic acid is composed of three pieces (a pterin, PABA and glutamic acid). These pieces fit perfectly onto the enzyme surface (A), and snap together forming folic acid. The completed molecule drops off the enzyme (B) and the process repeats (the key fits the lock and opens it).

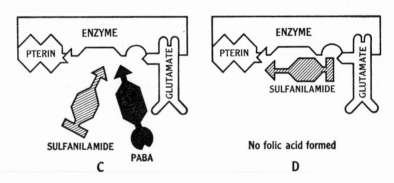

C

D

Sufanilamide is an analog (close chemical relative) of PABA. It competes with PABA for the enzyme site (C). Sulfa can attach to the enzyme surface, but the fit is imperfect (D) and it does not react with the pterin or the glutamic acid (the key fits the lock, but can't open it).

some important practical applications. It established a new principle in chemotherapy (the treatment of disease with chemical agents) called *competitive analog inhibition.* The competitive analog (sulfanilamide in our example) of the natural metabolite (PABA in our example) is usually called an *antimetabolite.*

Since sulfanilamide was found to be an antimetabolite of PABA, it was possible to predict what sort of other chemicals which are related to sulfanilamide might also be antimetabolites—and perhaps better than sulfanilamide. The organic chemists went to work and many new compounds were prepared—sulfathiazole, sulfapyridine, sulfadiazine, and sulfaguanidine, to mention only a few.

Some of these new synthetic sulfa drugs proved to be much more effective than sulfanilamide. For example, the growth of certain bacteria is halted if the fluid in which they are living contains 1,000 molecules of sulfanilamide for each molecule of PABA present. However, where 1,000 molecules of sulfanilamide are required to prevent growth 10 of sulfathiazole will suffice.

The availability of several different sulfa drugs of the sulfonamide type led to the solution of a difficult clinical problem. Sulfanilamide is not very soluble in acidic solutions. The acidity of blood is such that large amounts of sulfanilamide can be carried without any trouble. However, large doses were necessary for the inhibition of bacterial growth, and much of the sulfa was filtered out of the blood by the kidney. Often the sulfanilamide crystallized to form painful, and sometimes fatal, kidney stones.

With the development of more active sulfa drugs, it was possible to reduce the required dosage, which also lessened the chance of kidney stones. As soon as several sulfa drugs became available, the physician could prescribe a mixture of two or three sulfonamides. Since the effect of each was additive to the effect of the others, the amount of each sulfonamide could be decreased. In combinations, such as sulfanilamide-sulfathiazole, only half as much sulfanilamide would be required as when the drug was to be administered alone. Moreover, combination doses lessened the chance of kidney stone formation because the solubility of each sulfa is independent of the other sulfas and is dependent solely on its own concentration.

Recent work with antimetabolites suggests that they may be useful in connection with the control of cancer and certain mental disorders. Just what role anti-metabolites may play in these fields is only theory today, but additional research may ultimately give to mankind new tools and controls to some of his most perplexing problems.

7

FROM FOOD TO ENERGY

WHY DO WE EAT? Not just because we are hungry. Hunger is simply the body's way of signaling that it needs more raw materials to keep its chemical reactions going. Without these raw materials, which our food provides, the body could not function any more than an automobile factory could function without steel.

Everything we do—moving our arms and legs, talking, or even reading this page—requires energy. Food provides this energy, but if it were released all at once we would go up in smoke. In fact, an explosion is nothing more than a sudden release of a large amount of chemical energy. We don't explode because in the body, foodstuffs are converted to energy by a series of carefully controlled chemical reactions, each catalyzed by its own enzyme.

93

Intermediary metabolism is the study of these enzyme reactions—of what happens to food from the time it enters the body until it is excreted as waste products.

Long before the discovery of enzymes, however, men wondered what happened to food. We ingest several pounds of food and water every day and yet we do not gain any striking amount of weight in any one day. For 2,000 years Hippocrates and his successors said that the weight which was added through food and drink was lost in the urine, feces, and the "insensible perspiration." By insensible perspiration they meant the water vapor that is given off from the skin during perspiration and is exhaled from the lungs.

You can see insensible perspiration by breathing on a mirror; the fog you see is nothing more than water in the air you exhaled. We now know that insensible perspiration also contains carbon dioxide. So in a way the ancients were correct, since the food we eat can be accounted for in part by the carbon dioxide and water which are eliminated from the body. But the ancients had no idea what insensible perspiration was nor what really happened to food in the body.

First, men considered the role of the stomach in digestion. Hippocrates believed that it was little more than a stew pot and that the heat of the body cooked the food in the stomach. Others had other ideas, but none had experimental evidence to back their conclusions.

Then in the middle of the eighteenth century, a distinguished seventy-year-old Frenchman named Réamur decided to investigate this problem of the digestion of food. Réamur had a pet kite (a bird of the hawk family) which had a strange habit: it would regurgitate anything it swallowed that it could not digest. Réamur decided to capitalize on his pet's strange characteristic. He took a small metal flask and punctured holes in its sides. Then he put pieces of meat into the flask and forced the kite to swallow the flask. Of course, the kite couldn't digest the metal flask, so before long, up it came. And the amazing thing was that the meat inside the flask had changed and was now partly dissolved.

Réamur carried out another experiment. He knew that kites did not like sponges so he reasoned that in all probability they could not digest them. He cut a sponge into small pieces and put the pieces into a flask which he forced the kite to swallow. As before, the kite regurgitated it. Here before him were sponges almost five times heavier than when he had put them into the flask. And these sponges were filled with a liquid which obviously came from the kite's stomach. He named this liquid *gastric juice* (from the Greek *gastēr,* stomach).

But he was not finished. Next, he took the pieces of sponge and washed them to make sure no dissolved food was lodged in them. Then he waited until the kite was hungry and its stomach empty. Once again he forced the clean sponges down the kite's throat. This time when the kite regurgitated the sponges, Réamur squeezed the juice into glass tubes, keeping the juice at body temperature. He found that this strange juice could dissolve meat, seeds and even small pieces of bone. From these experiments, Réamur concluded that the stomach is not a stew pot, but a chemical factory that needs gastric juice to complete its work. This venerable scientist was the first to collect samples of gastric juice and to show by experiment that this powerful liquid can also do its work of digesting materials outside the body.

Another milestone in our understanding of digestion came from an unusual accident. It happened on Mackinac Island in northern Lake Michigan. Besides being a U.S. Army post hospital, the island was also a trading post of the American Fur Company. Each year this company hired many men as *voyageurs* to transport men and goods to remote stations for trapping fur-bearing animals.

On June 6, 1822, a French Canadian *voyageur,* Alexis St. Martin, was accidentally shot with a musket at short range at the trading post. The shot tore open a large hole in his abdomen. A young Army surgeon, Dr. William Beaumont, rushed in to care for him, took one look at his protruding lungs and what appeared as ripped pieces of stomach and thought the patient hopelessly wounded. He administered first aid and cut away some of the protruding flesh with a penknife and had the patient carried to the simple hospital in a nearby shack. He worked on the gaping wound but could not completely close it surgically. Much to his amazement, St. Martin survived —with a permanent fistula, or opening, in his stomach.

Dr. Beaumont worked heroically to save his patient; operation followed operation and great care was given in the dressing and draining of the slowly healing wound. For months the town officials supported St. Martin, but after a time they were ready to ship him back to his native Canada by open boat.

Beaumont decided that this freak accident offered a unique opportunity to study the workings of a human stomach so he took the youth into his own home where he continued to care for him and to observe this stomach with the "open window." St. Martin was not a particularly reliable subject. He was sometimes difficult to get along with and grew restless at times. On several occasions he left Dr. Beaumont without a word, but fortunately he always returned.

And so for many years this U.S. Army Medical Corps doctor had a human guinea pig in St. Martin. He even took St. Martin along with him when he was transferred to Fort Niagara, and continued to study the functioning of the human stomach with the aid of its permanent opening. Beaumont learned a great deal about what happens to food in the stomach from the one hundred sixteen experiments he conducted on his patient. And he must have learned a great deal about human relations, too, because three years after the accident, St. Martin ran away into the Canadian backwoods and absented himself for four years. When he returned, he brought along a wife and their two young children. In return for the support of the family, St. Martin consented to allow Dr. Beaumont to continue his experiments.

He wanted to know more about those stomach juices

but realized that he lacked the training for this work. So he tried to get the help of other physicians. He took St. Martin to New York, but found a disappointing lack of interest in physiological chemistry. Next he journeyed to Yale University where he was advised to send a bottle of St. Martin's stomach juices to the great Berzelius in Sweden. He did this, but there is no record of its being received or of any exchange of thinking between the leading Swedish chemist and the lonely outpost doctor in the New World.

By this time Beaumont was used to disappointments and prepared to carry on his experiments alone—without suitable equipment, specialized training, or the interest of other medical men in his patient or his work. Dr. Beaumont carried on his many experiments at his own expense, testing the influence of thirst, hunger, and taste on the secretion of the digestive juices. For example, he found that the stomach poured out gastric juice when St. Martin swallowed food naturally. However, this did not happen when food was put into the stomach through the fistula. Thus, the presence of food in the mouth seemed to stimulate the flow of gastric juice. (He antedated the work of the Russian physiologist Pavlov by many years.)

Beaumont obtained samples of gastric juice which were clear and odorless. This liquid was salty, just as Réamur had said. It contained free hydrochloric acid as well as other chemical substances. He also found that the food had disappeared from the stomach about four hours after eating and that food introduced through the fistula abolished hunger pains.

Beaumont's discovery of the potency of the stomach's juices cleared away all of the earlier conceptions of the mechanism of digestion. Certainly the stomach is no stew pot or grinding mill but rather an organ capable of making a powerful substance which can dissolve and disintegrate any food that is eaten. But it was several years before Schwann discovered the first component of the stomach's juice and named it *pepsin*—an enzyme which partially digests proteins.

Today, through the efforts of many scientists over a period of more than a hundred years, most of the mysteries of the digestion of food have been solved. Like many other body functions, this is mainly an enzymatic process which begins in the mouth and ends with the absorption of the digested food by the walls of the intestines.

Imagine that we have just made a ham sandwich using bread (carbohydrate), butter (fat), lettuce (carbohydrate), and ham (protein and fat). The sight of this sandwich stimulates the salivary glands to secrete saliva so that the mouth waters. We take a bite of the sandwich and chew it; the teeth grind up the food and mix it with saliva so that it forms a kind of ball called a *bolus*. The saliva contains the enzyme *ptylin,* or *alpha amylase* as it is usually called today, which begins to break down the large starch molecules in the bread to smaller units. The only digestion which takes place in the mouth is the partial breakdown of starch. But alpha amylase doesn't have long to act because most of us swallow our sandwich after a few quick chews. The food bolus is then carried down to the stomach where it is mixed with the gastric juice and the hydrochloric acid present in the gastric juice inactivates the alpha amylase.

Lettuce, which is mainly water (95 per cent) but also contains carbohydrate, is not digested by alpha amylase because the carbohydrate in lettuce is primarily cellulose. This carbohydrate is also composed of glucose building blocks, but they are hooked together a little differently than in starch. Because of the specificity of alpha amylase, it is unable to break down the cellulose molecule.

Like human juices, a cow's digestive juices lack an enzyme capable of breaking down cellulose. Yet the cow thrives on a diet mainly of grass which is mostly cellulose. However, the cow would starve on this fare if it were not for the fact that her stomachs (four) contain a large population of bacteria which have an enzyme capable of degrading cellulose. These bacteria break down the cellulose, and the glucose units which result are absorbed and utilized in the usual manner.

The major part of digestion occurring in the stomach is the partial breakdown of protein by pepsin. Perhaps you wonder why the stomach doesn't dissolve itself. After all, it is composed partly of protein. We know that both pepsin and strong hydrochloric acid which are present in the stomach during digestion can hydrolyze proteins, but

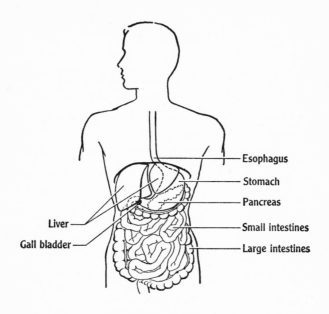

DIGESTIVE SYSTEM

we are not sure why the acid and pepsin don't attack the wall of the stomach. It may be partly because its wall is coated with a material called *mucin* which appears to protect the stomach from self-digestion. Of course, there is a great deal more to it than this simple explanation. The complete answer to this problem is of prime interest to the medical profession because it would appear that a breakdown of the protective mechanism, whatever it is, is the cause of peptic ulcers.

Besides its function in the breakdown of proteins, the

stomach is an important site of mechanical digestion. Here the gentle wavelike motions of the stomach, called *peristalsis,* mix and churn the food and the gastric juice until they are homogenized to the consistency of a thick cream, called *chyme.* The food is now ready for the final stages of digestion in the small intestine.

The chyme passes from the stomach into the intestine and mixes with the intestinal secretions. The intestinal juice is composed of three main components: bile from the liver—which emulsifies fats so that the lipases (enzymes which attack fats) can digest them to glycerol and fatty acids; enzymes from the pancreas—proteases, carbohydrases and lipases, all acting to move digestion closer to completion; and enzymes from the wall of the intestine—which complete digestion.

Thus, the main food substances in our sandwich have been reduced to simple units: starch to glucose (mouth and intestine), protein to amino acids (stomach and intestine) and fat to glycerol plus fatty acids (intestine). These simple units are absorbed from the intestine by processes which are still not completely understood, and are carried by the circulatory system (blood and lymph) to the cells of the body. In the cells they are used either to build up essential cellular constituents, such as protein (anabolism), or are broken down to provide energy for the body (catabolism). The whole process in which the simple food units are utilized by the cells is called *metabolism.* The food which is not digested, for example cellulose, cannot be absorbed and passes out of the body as feces.

So far we have traced the food into the body. The story of its further fate is the story of metabolism. This begins in the seventeenth century with Robert Boyle, English chemist, sometimes known as the Father of Chemistry. Boyle demonstrated that animals have to have air to live. In essence, his experiment was a simple one. He placed a small mouse in a round, eight-ounce vial with a wide neck. A thin bladder was fastened securely to the neck of the vial after carefully pressing all of the air out of the bladder. This "phantastical vessel" was placed inside another vessel. Air was pumped from this outer vessel until about a fourth of the original air remained. Since the pressure in the outer vessel was now less than inside the small vial in which the mouse resided, the air in the vial expanded and Boyle observed that the bladder was "blown almost half full." The pressure of the oxygen in this inner vial was then about half of its normal value in air and the mouse began to experience oxygen lack, much as if one were to fly at high altitude without any oxygen.

Boyle wrote, "The mouse seeming ill at ease by his leaping, and otherwise endeavoring to pass out at the neck of his uneasy prison; we did, for fear the over thin air would dispatch him, let the air flow into the external receiver, whereby the bladder being compressed, and the air in the vial reduced to its former density, the little animal quickly recovered."

He repeated the experiment. If no fresh air was let into the vial the mouse died in about an hour. When Boyle put another mouse into the vial to replace the first one which had died, the second mouse died within three minutes. So it was obvious that animals require air for life. Something was used in breathing which could not be used a second time.

A hundred years passed before chemistry had progressed sufficiently for a different kind of air to be recognized. In the eighteenth century, Joseph Black, a Scottish physician who became interested in chemistry as a medical student and eventually became professor of Chemistry at the University of Edinburgh, discovered carbon dioxide, or, as he called it, "fixed air."

Soon afterward, Joseph Priestley, an English chemist, and a Swedish apothecary-chemist named Karl Scheele discovered oxygen, or as Scheele called it, "fire air." They found that oxygen was necessary for life.

Scheele took two bees and placed them in a glass chamber with a little honey. Then he connected the chamber to a cylinder full of oxygen and inverted it in a dish of lime-water. The carbon dioxide expired by the bees was heavier than air and so it sank to the bottom of the cylinder and was absorbed by the lime-water. Each day as the bees used up the oxygen in the chamber the total volume of air (a mixture of carbon dioxide and oxygen) in the cylinder decreased and the lime-water rose higher and higher. At the end of the week the lime-water almost filled the cylinder and the bees were dead. These experiments showed that living things give off carbon dioxide and require oxygen to stay alive.

Both Priestley and Scheele were in communication with Lavoisier and, at their request, he repeated their experiments and confirmed their results. But it remained for Lavoisier to synthesize the current concepts and advance our understanding of respiration.

One of Lavoisier's most brilliant experiments was done in collaboration with the French mathematician Laplace. They put a guinea pig into the inner chamber of a calorimeter and then measured the carbon dioxide produced by the animal's respiration during a ten-hour period. Next they burned carbon in a closed vessel and found that when three and one-third grams of carbon were oxidized, it liberated the same amount of carbon dioxide as the guinea pig during ten hours of respiration in the vessel. Thus, they concluded that during the ten-hour period the guinea pig had converted the equivalent of three and one-third grams of its body carbon to carbon dioxide.

They knew that when three and one-third grams of carbon were oxidized to carbon dioxide a definite amount of heat was liberated because when they surrounded the combustion chamber with a known amount of ice, the same amount of ice was melted each time. Was there a similar relationship between the carbon dioxide expired by the guinea pig and the heat which its body gave off?

They confined the guinea pig in a chamber surrounded

by ice and after ten hours determined how much ice had melted. Within experimental error, *the same amount of ice was melted by the guinea pig in ten hours as when three and a third grams of carbon were burned to carbon dioxide.* This experiment established for the first time that there is a direct relationship between the amount of heat produced by a living organism and the amount of carbon dioxide it expires.

Lavoisier went on to study human subjects by having them breathe into a mask which was connected to various devices. This allowed him to measure the amount of oxygen they used and the amount of carbon dioxide which they expired under a variety of conditions. From these studies Lavoisier concluded, "Respiration is only a slow combustion of carbon and hydrogen which is similar in all respects to that which takes place in a lamp or a lighted candle; and from this point of view animals which respire are truly combustible bodies which burn and consume themselves."

Unfortunately we do not know exactly how Lavoisier carried out these experiments because he was dragged off to the guillotine and executed by French Revolutionists for his loyalty to the Crown before he could publish his work in full. But he was remarkably near the truth. He believed that heat is produced in the body by oxidation of foodstuffs in the lungs. Many years were to pass before it was shown that this actually does take place in the various tissues of the body.

The next important step in understanding metabolic

processes came in 1841 when Mayer formulated the law of the conservation of energy or as it is usually called today, *the first law of thermodynamics.* According to this law *the sum total of all the energy in the universe remains constant,* but one form of energy may be converted to another.

Shortly after, others performed experiments which showed that heat and work are interconvertible. Thus, energy manifests itself as either heat or work. For example, if one coils a piece of steel into a spring, work is expended. The work is transferred to the coiled spring and is stored as potential energy. So the coil of steel has more energy than it did as a straight length of metal. This is easily proved. If the coiled spring is dissolved in acid, more heat is evolved than when an uncoiled length of steel of the same dimensions is dissolved in acid.

Our confidence in the first law of thermodynamics arises mainly from the fact that no exceptions have yet been found. But would this law hold for living organisms, experimenters asked. The work of Lavoisier suggested that it would, but more rigorous proof was needed. If the law of conservation of energy was correct, it should be possible under the proper experimental conditions to account for the energy taken in food (chemical energy) in terms of heat given off by the experimental animal. But first it was necessary to know what the chemical energy for the three types of foods—protein, carbohydrate, and fat—was in terms of heat.

About the middle of the nineteenth century a physiology professor at Marburg by the name of Rubner made some measurements, outside the body, of the heat content of foodstuffs. When he oxidized purified carbohydrate in a calorimeter, he found that the heat liberated was about 4 Calories per gram. Then he constructed a calorimeter large enough to accommodate a full-grown dog. He placed the dog in the calorimeter and fed him measured rations of food for several days. At the same time he carefully measured the heat liberated by the animal and also collected the urine and feces, analyzing each for its nitrogen content and calculating its heat content. From these data, he was able to calculate that, within experimental error, the heat liberated by the oxidation of the food in the dog was the same as in the bomb calorimeter for carbohydrate and fat.

When he studied the proteins, however, he found a discrepancy. In the dog only 4 Calories per gram were liberated, but in the bomb calorimeter more than 5 Calories per gram were set free. Fortunately, the explanation was a simple one. Protein is completely oxidized in the bomb calorimeter, but not in the body, and the nitrogen is excreted as urea and other nitrogenous products. When a correction for the heat content of these excreted materials was applied, it was found that the heat values for protein, both inside and outside the body, checked. From these studies Rubner obtained values which are still used today in nutritional studies: Protein, 4.1 Calories/gram; carbohydrate, 4.1 Calories/gram; fat, 9.3 Calories/gram.

Thus, the law of conservation of energy was clearly established in a living organism. Rubner also furnished final confirmation of the results that Lavoisier had obtained almost 100 years earlier.

During his student days Rubner had worked with a respiration chamber built by his teacher, Carl Voit, and the physicist Pettenkofer. This chamber was large enough to accommodate a dog. Rubner had engaged in studies in which he measured the oxygen uptake and carbon dioxide output of experimental animals under various conditions. Now he put this early training to good use. He hooked a respiration chamber to his calorimeter and measured the heat output as well as the uptake of oxygen and output of carbon dioxide. His heat measurements agreed within 1 per cent of the values he had calculated from the oxygen and carbon dioxide measurements.

More elaborate confirmation of the law of the conservation of energy was obtained with human subjects by Atwater, another pupil of Voit's. He constructed the first respiration calorimeter large enough to accommodate a man. He installed a bicycle inside the calorimeter in order to demonstrate the conversion of energy to work. Attached to the bicycle was an *ergometer,* an instrument which enabled him to measure the work, in terms of heat, the subject did in riding the bicycle. He found that the energy content of the food given the subject was always equal to his heat output (corrected for excretions) plus the energy output during exercise, as measured by the ergometer. This established conclusively that in the human, energy equals heat plus work, just as the first law of thermodynamics predicted.

Using this technique of *direct calorimetry,* it has been found that a resting male subject in the postabsorptive state liberates about 1,500 to 1,800 Calories a day. This represents the energy which is necessary to keep the vital functions of the body going (such as the heart beat) and is called the *basic metabolic rate.* Direct respiration calorimeters, however, although simple in theory, are so difficult to build and expensive to operate that only a few are in existence. With these machines it has been conclusively demonstrated that the energy calculated from the oxygen consumption of a subject under basal metabolic conditions is exactly equal to the heat given off by his body. Thus, it is possible to dispense with the calorimeter and determine the heat output of a subject simply by measuring the gaseous exchange during respiration. This is called *indirect calorimetry.*

Indirect calorimeter machines are in wide use today in hospitals and clinical laboratories. If you have ever had your basal metabolism taken, you will remember just how they work. First the subject must fast for twelve hours before taking the test. Upon arrival for the test the subject lies quietly for about a half hour before the measurements are begun. This allows him maximum mental and muscular rest without being asleep. Then a clip is placed over the subject's nose, and a mouthpiece, which is connected to the machine, is placed in his mouth. The subject is told to breathe normally—an instruction much easier to give than follow since the subject is apt to think that he'll never breathe normally again. Normal breathing does take place, however, and the carbon dioxide which he expires is absorbed by a canister of soda lime so that the only actual measurement made is that of oxygen consumption. From appropriate data about the subject, such as age, sex, weight and height, plus the oxygen consumption, it is possible to calculate the basal metabolic rate or BMR, as it is called.

A knowledge of the BMR helps the physician to diagnose certain pathological conditions. For example, high BMR's are associated with diseases such as hyperthyroidism (overactive thyroid gland) and leukemia (cancer of the blood); low BMR's are linked with such diseases as Addison's disease (loss of function of part of the adrenal glands) and hypothyroidism (underactive thyroid gland).

Indirect calorimetry is also used by the nutritionist to study the kind of food we need to eat and how much we need to eat for adequate nutrition. So you can see that Lavoisier and Laplace really started something with their calorimeter studies.

Today we have a considerable body of information concerning the digestion of food. And we know the energy values of thousands of different foods, as you well know if you have counted the Calories in your daily diet in order to gain or lose weight. In other words, we have knowledge about what happens to food during the over-all process of metabolism. We know the beginning and end, but what happens in between? How is food energy released in the body, and more important, how is it har-nessed by the body to do useful work, such as reading this page or using muscles for more active purposes? At-tempts to answer such questions have formed the very core of biochemistry for the last fifty years and are the subject of *intermediary metabolism*.

Chapter 8

CARBOHYDRATE METABOLISM
A GIANT JIGSAW PUZZLE

WHEN A CAR runs out of gas it stops because the engine needs fuel to run. Even with gas in the tank, if it runs long enough it stops because it wears out. Living organisms behave in the same way. They can't operate without fuel (food) and when they wear out they die. When the engine in a car runs out of gas we simply fill up the gas tank, or when the engine wears out we can replace it with a new one. Most living cells, however, are not so easily repaired. In general, they are really very fragile machines; if they are deprived of fuel for very long they die. Or if one of the important parts of the cell is worn out or damaged it is often impossible to replace it and the cell dies. Fortunately, living organisms can reproduce new cells. We've all watched a cut finger heal—new cells are made to close the wound. In fact, many of the cells in our body are continuously dying and new ones take their place.

It requires work to rebuild an engine, and work requires an energy source. In the same way, rebuilding cells requires energy and when they are built, it takes energy to keep them running. Food, of course, supplies this energy, but imagine how inconvenient it would be if we had to eat constantly, night and day. Simple organisms, such as bacteria, actually do this, but, higher organisms, such as man, have developed storage systems, very much like the gas tank in a car, which need only to be "filled up" periodically.

The food we eat in a meal contains far more energy than our cells can use all at once. The body saves up this extra food in several ways. For example, carbohydrates are stored in the liver and muscles as a starchlike material called *glycogen*. Fat is deposited in special areas called adipose tissue. Even tissue protein represents an emergency energy source. In between meals, these stores furnish cell food which is distributed throughout the body by the blood.

This constant supply of energy is used not only to build new cells, but also to carry out a large number of special body functions. Without energy we couldn't move our muscles or, for that matter, even read this page. In fact, the most important process which living cells carry out is energy production, but they must do this in a very special way. If they were to release the energy too fast, they would burn themselves up. But even a controlled release of energy is not enough because the cells need their energy in a special form before they can use it. In a steam engine, for example, heat (a common form of energy) can be used to boil water and the steam produced can be used to drive a piston and do work. But living cells can't use heat energy because they have no way of converting heat into work. In living organisms, heat is actually a waste product—it represents energy which the cells have failed to use.

So living organisms must have a way of releasing energy gradually and in usable form. Scientists began studying this process by measuring the energy content of food and waste products, that is, the beginning and the end of metabolism. But these experiments didn't solve the most important problem—what happens in between? The famous French physiologist Claude Bernard summed up this approach by saying, "This is like trying to find out what goes on inside a house by watching what goes in the door and what comes out the chimney."

Bernard was one of the first scientists to study the in-between reactions which are responsible for *intermediary metabolism*. That was almost a century ago, and since then biochemists have made remarkable progress in piecing this giant jigsaw puzzle together. Today we know that energy is released from our food by an extremely complex series of enzymatic reactions. These reactions have been studied in great detail and now it is possible to answer puzzling questions such as: Why do we need oxygen to live? Where does the carbon dioxide we exhale come from?

We know that carbohydrates play a vital role in intermediary metabolism. Not only do they supply cellular building materials, but they represent an important energy source. However, this energy is locked tightly in the carbohydrate molecules and the question is: How is this energy released in the body? Let's consider the important carbohydrate, glucose. Imagine twenty-four tiny balls (the atoms which make up a glucose molecule) held together by springs. Each ball also has a set of hooks so the balls can be pushed together, compressing the springs, and then held in this position by the hooks. Of course, it takes energy to compress the springs and when the balls are hooked together this energy is stored in the compressed spring bonds waiting to be released. We can demonstrate this by simply unhooking the balls. Now there is nothing holding the balls together and the energy in the compressed springs is released causing the balls to fly apart.

A similar situation exists in a chemical molecule, such as glucose. Considerable energy has been used in pressing the atoms which form glucose together and this energy is stored in the chemical bonds between atoms. If we put glucose into a strong metal container, such as a bomb calorimeter, introduce some oxygen and then explode the mixture with a spark, the atoms of each glucose molecule will fly apart. The carbon atoms from the glucose combine with oxygen to form carbon dioxide and the hydrogen atoms combine with oxygen to form water. However, the energy which can be stored in carbon dioxide and water is much less than in the glucose molecule so energy is set free and, in this case, it appears as heat.

The cells of our body also obtain energy by oxidizing glucose to carbon dioxide and water. This is why we need oxygen to live and it is the source of carbon dioxide we exhale. But in living cells the process is slow and controlled, instead of explosive, and only part of the energy is released immediately as heat—just enough to keep the body warm. The rest is converted to a more useful form.

The chemical reactions which are responsible for energy release are too complex to consider in detail here. However, we can picture the overall process by borrowing an analogy from the Nobel Laureate Fritz Lipmann. Let's think of the enzymatic reactions which carry out oxidation as an electrical dynamo.

In this mechanical model, water spins the turbine which, in turn, drives the electrical generator. The electricity which is produced can be used to run a motor, produce light or heat, and so on. Thus, the energy liberated by water running down hill is converted to a more useful form, electricity.

In the body, the energy stored in glucose must also be converted to a more usable form. We can picture this process as a "metabolic dynamo," which, like our mechanical model, is composed of a "turbine" and a "generator."

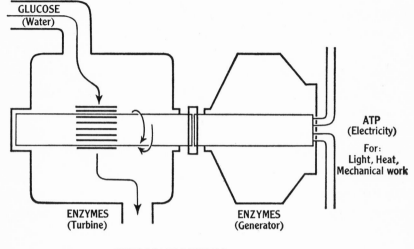

METABOLIC DYNAMO

First a series of enzymes splits the glucose molecules in half to prepare them for the turbine. This step is represented by the flow of water in our mechanical model. The glucose fragments then pass into the turbine which, in reality, is a collection of nine different enzymes. As the molecules are passed from one enzyme to another, the chemical bonds are broken releasing energy and converting the original glucose carbon atoms to carbon dioxide. This carbon dioxide is carried from the tissue cells to the lungs by the blood and exhaled as we breathe. This is the origin of respiratory carbon dioxide.

However, the energy released by the turbine process is still not in the proper form, so it is transferred to the generator. The generator is also a collection of very remarkable enzymes which requires oxygen to make the conversion to usable energy. Largely because of this we need oxygen to live.

In the generator, the energy which was originally locked in the glucose molecule is transferred to a special chemical called *adenosine triphosphate* or, as biochemists abbreviate it, ATP. In the metabolic dynamo ATP is analogous to the electrical current produced by the electrical dynamo. Just as electricity can be used to do mechanical work or produce light, ATP can be used to contract muscles (mechanical work), produce light (fireflies), and so on. ATP, then, is the immediate energy source of almost all processes which living systems carry out.

The body uses this complicated process to release energy in just the right way, but the overall process is no different than when carbohydrate is burned in a calorimeter. Both processes require oxygen and both produce carbon dioxide and water—only the methods of producing these products are different. So we can represent the process as:

$$\text{carbohydrate} + \text{oxygen} \rightleftharpoons \text{water} + \text{carbon dioxide} + \text{energy}$$

Under the proper conditions this process can be reversed. Green plants, for example, can combine carbon dioxide and water to form carbohydrate and oxygen. Of course, this conversion requires energy and this energy comes from the *light* of the sun. This process is called *photosynthesis.* Photosynthetic organisms have special compounds such as *chlorophyll,* to trap light energy. One of the most interesting problems in modern biochemistry is how these light traps actually work.

One might easily get the impression that the metabolism of plants and animals is completely different. But this is not true—for the most part, the same chemical

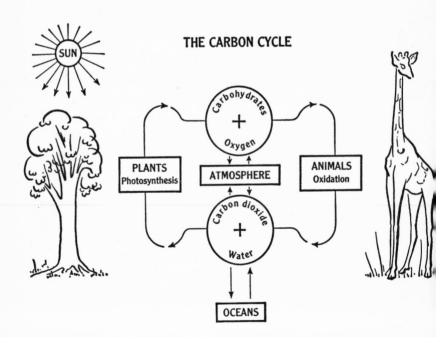

THE CARBON CYCLE

reactions occur in *all* living cells, plant or animal. However, photosynthetic organisms can use light as an energy source while other organisms, such as man, cannot. This enables photosynthetic organisms to exist on a very simple diet—carbon dioxide and water in the case of green plants. In turn, we depend upon plants to supply chemical substances which our cells need to function. We obtain carbohydrates, for example, from plant foods in our diet and we oxidize them to carbon dioxide and water to obtain energy. So the cycle is complete.

This so-called *carbon cycle* illustrates the basis for coexistence of plant and animal life on the earth. However, it emphasizes the differences between these two basic forms of living organisms and tends to obscure the similarities in their metabolism. For example, plants make starch by hooking glucose molecules together into long chains. Similarly, animals produce a kind of starch called *glycogen* which is also composed of chains of glucose. Furthermore, glycogen is the storage form of glucose in animals, just as starch is in plants. One of the most exciting biochemical discoveries of the century came when Carl and Gerty Cori, a husband and wife team, isolated a pure, crystalline enzyme from muscle which catalyzed the formation of glycogen in the test tube. For their brilliant work the Coris received the Nobel Prize in 1947. A similar enzyme which catalyzed the synthesis of starch from glucose was isolated from potatoes. Subsequent work has established that the enzymatic reactions catalyzed by phosphorylase in animals or in plants are almost identical.

There are many more examples of the similarities between the metabolic reactions of animals and higher plants, but what about the other major division of the living world, microorganisms? Again we find many features of both plant and animal metabolism. For example, some bacteria, like plants, are photosynthetic. Others, like animals, require their carbohydrates in ready-made form. Perhaps one of the most striking metabolic similarities between microorganisms and animals is a process called *glycolysis*. In fact, this important metabolic process was discovered in yeast long ago; we know it by another name, fermentation. In yeast, glucose is fermented to alcohol and carbon dioxide by a series of enzyme reactions. Glycolysis in animal cells proceeds by exactly the same reactions except for the last step. Thus, in animals, glucose is converted to lactic acid instead of alcohol and carbon dioxide.

Biochemists often make use of the fact that different kinds of cells have basically the same metabolic reactions. A famous experiment will illustrate this point. Otto Meyerhof, a German biochemist, was studying the metabolism of carbohydrates in frog muscle extracts. When freshly prepared these extracts would convert glucose or glycogen to lactic acid. But after a time the extract lost its ability to metabolize glucose though it continued to convert glycogen to lactic acid. Obviously, something was being destroyed as the extract aged. Meyerhof was well aware of the similarities between yeast and muscle metabolism so he prepared a yeast extract and added it to the aged muscle juice. Glucose was again utilized and lactic acid was formed from it.

Next Meyerhof placed some yeast cells in a mixture of water and toluene which caused the cells to burst and liberate their contents. Then he removed the debris by centrifugation. Addition of alcohol to the clear solution precipitated a substance which was soluble in water and inactivated by heat. When this substance was added to aged muscle extracts, glucose was rapidly converted to lactic acid. Further studies showed that this material was an enzyme which Meyerhof named *hexokinase*.

Animal hexokinase is destroyed much more easily than yeast hexokinase and during the aging of the muscle juice it loses its biological activity. Since this enzyme is required for conversion of glucose to lactic acid, the inability of aged muscle extracts to metabolize glucose is easily explained.

Hexokinase was the first single enzyme to be isolated from extracts which glycolyzed glucose and it became clear that the extracts were not single enzymes but mixtures. Since then biochemists have isolated and purified all the enzymes which are necessary for the conversion of glucose or glycogen to lactic acid in animal tissues or carbon dioxide and alcohol in yeast. The reactions which they catalyze have been studied in detail so that now glycolysis can be reconstructed in a test tube from purified enzymes, some coenzymes and glucose. In this way biochemists have fitted part of the puzzle of carbohydrate metabolism together and the riddle of fermentation in yeast and glycolysis in animals has been solved at last.

In order to understand how an engine runs it is necessary to take it apart and find out what each part does. This is equivalent to taking a cell apart and studying the individual enzyme reactions which it carries out. If we have interpreted the workings of the individual engine parts correctly we should be able to use this information to explain how the intact engine operates. Similarly, if we have properly pieced together the isolated enzymatic reactions, we should be able to explain how they work in the cell to carry out some process. This is really the biochemist's goal —to explain the workings of living cells in terms of a collection of chemical reactions. Let's see what we can do with our information to explain what happens during muscle contraction.

We know that a large portion of the energy derived from food is used to contract muscles—to move arms and legs, to keep the heart beating and so on. We also know that this food energy is converted to ATP and therefore the logical hypothesis is that ATP furnishes the energy for muscle contraction. We also need to know something about muscle itself.

Chemically speaking there is nothing very spectacular about muscle. It is composed of protein (about 18 per cent), small amounts of glycogen and other organic compounds, traces of minerals, and water (about 80 per cent). Under the microscope, muscle appears as regularly arranged bundles of fibers. However, the major protein in these fibers is rather special. It is called *actomyosin*. When a salt solution of this protein is squirted through a syringe into water, long threads, which look just like a muscle fiber, are formed. If ATP is added to the solution in which the fibers are bathing, they contract. Nobel Prize winner Albert Szent-Györgyi, who performed this experiment, writes, "To see actomyosin contract was one of the greatest impressions of my scientific career. Motion is one of the most basic biological phenomena and has always been looked upon as the index of life. Now we could produce it in a test tube with constituents of the cell."

The experiments of Szent-Györgyi and many other biochemists support the hypothesis that ATP causes actomyosin to contract and that this is the basis for muscle contraction. But we still don't know exactly how this occurs. There are still some important pieces missing from the puzzle. However, we can explain many things with our present knowledge. As an example, let's consider a mile run at a track meet.

On your mark—get set—go! The runners explode from the starting line, their muscles straining hard. ATP is being used up rapidly to furnish energy for contraction, but everything is under control since the muscles have plenty of oxygen to make more ATP by oxidizing carbohydrate through the "dynamo." As the runners reach the first turn, their strides smooth out. They breathe a little deeper now to increase the supply of oxygen to their muscles and also to get rid of the increasing amounts of carbon dioxide formed by the oxidation of carbohydrates. Soon they breathe fast and deep, their hearts pound furiously as blood is pumped through the body. But it is of no use; the generator is running at top speed but the muscles are using up ATP faster than it can be replaced. Slowly, the ATP stores begin to dwindle. Lactic acid begins to pile up—muscle fatigue is commencing.

They can't keep up this furious pace much longer. They cross the finish line and it is all over! The runners slow quickly; their muscles ache with fatigue (the energy source, ATP, is depleted and lactic acid content is high). They gasp for breath to increase the oxygen supply to the tissues so that ATP can be resynthesized by oxidative metabolism. Their hearts pound as blood is pumped rapidly through the body removing the lactic acid from the muscles and carrying it to the liver where it is converted back to glucose. The blood leaving the liver carries glucose back to the muscles where it is stored as glycogen until needed. And pretty soon this remarkable machine is back to normal as if nothing had ever happened. On a lesser scale this is what happens every time you run for a bus or swim or engage in any kind of muscular activity.

These are some of the highlights in the fascinating field of carbohydrate metabolism. Extraordinary progress in unraveling this giant jigsaw puzzle has been made in the last twenty-five years and yet we still have many questions to answer. These answers will have to await new experiments, new techniques, and new ideas.

Chapter 9

FATS

THE ENERGY STOREHOUSE

THE LENGTH OF TIME a person can survive without food depends upon his physical condition. One of the longest successful fasts on record was by the professional faster Merlatte of Paris who went without food for fifty days. During a fast such as this as much as 25 per cent of the body weight, mainly fat, may be lost.

An average man has less than one pound of glycogen in his body. This represents about 1,500 Calories—less than enough for one day's supply of energy. This same man, however, will have about 27 pounds of fat. This represents more than 100,000 Calories—enough for a sedentary existence of nine to ten weeks without food.

There is a good reason why fat is the main energy store in the body rather than protein or carbohydrate. We have already seen that oxidation of one gram of fat produces about 9 Calories, while oxidation of a gram of carbohydrate or protein produces only about 4 Calories. So weight would increase as much as 35 pounds if the normal supply of Calories was stored as carbohydrate or protein rather than fat.

Another interesting reason for storing energy as fat goes back to prehistoric organisms which inhabited the earth an estimated billion years ago. These early forms of life were undoubtedly simple unicellular organisms which slowly evolved in response to a changing environment into more complicated organisms. Eventually, primitive fish evolved, and, about 350 million years ago, some of these aquatic creatures left the sea to live on land. Since they had developed a functional existence in water they were still dependent upon it. This state of evolution is represented today by the amphibians, such as frogs and salamanders, which are unable to live out of water for very long.

The reptiles—the snakes and lizards—represent the first truly terrestrial animals. They evolved from amphibians and, by developing a dry skin which could retain their body water, they were able to attain a completely earthly existence. However, the reptiles and the evolutionary offshoots—birds and mammals—are still aquatic organisms. The human body is about 70–80 per cent water, and the body fluids still maintain the major characteristics of sea water with respect to salt composition.

The chemical reactions of the body require an aqueous

environment. Since water is lost continuously through the skin, lungs, and excretions, it must be continuously replaced. The body has several regulating devices to keep the water content constant. Thirst, for example, is a signal that the body needs more water.

Animals which must exist for long periods of time without drinking any water rely heavily on the oxidation of fat to supply them with energy. Oxidation of fat supplies much more water as an end product than does the oxidation of carbohydrate or protein. The reason for this lies in the chemical nature of fats, which contain a much higher percentage of hydrogen atoms per gram than carbohydrates or proteins. During oxidation, the hydrogen atoms combine with oxygen to form water.

The egg laid by a chicken contains only a small amount of water, which by itself would be insufficient to see the chick embryo through its development. However, during the three-week incubation period, more than 90 per cent of the material oxidized to yield energy for the chick's growth is fat. This fat oxidation supplies the necessary water.

The almost legendary ability of the camel to go for long periods of time without water is partly due to fat metabolism. The camel's hump does not contain water, *per se,* but fat. So the camel's hump is in reality an energy depot with a large water supply.

Chemically, fats are composed of a molecule of glycerol (glycerine) to which three molecules of fatty acids are attached. Because of this relatively simple structure, it is not surprising that much of the chemistry of fats was worked out long before that of carbohydrates and proteins. Chevreul, a French chemist, pioneered research in fat chemistry from 1813 to 1823. One of his interesting experiments involved the boiling of fats with alkali. From this combination he obtained glycerol and alkali salts of various fatty acids. We make use of Chevreul's discovery many times a day because these fatty acid salts are *soaps* —hence the formation of soap from fat is called *saponification* (from Latin *sapo,* soap).

Saponification of fats also occurs during the digestion of fats in the small intestine of the body, but in this process, instead of boiling with a strong alkali, the reaction is brought about by enzymes which are called *lipases.*

However, before a fat can be digested it must be dissolved in an aqueous intestinal fluid which contains lipases. As you know from dishwashing, fats are not very soluble in water. When a detergent is added to the wash water the large fat drops are broken into many tiny droplets which dissolve more easily. The body has its own set of natural detergents, the *bile salts,* which are made in the liver and stored in the gall bladder. They enter the intestine during digestion and help the fats to dissolve so that the lipases can digest them.

How fats are absorbed from the intestines is a question which still puzzles biochemists. Regardless of how this occurs, we do know that fat is stored in the adipose tissue.

For a long time it was believed that fat was stored in the body in a static state until it was needed for metabolism. However, isotopic experiments proved this to be false. These studies were done with *deuterium,* the heavy isotope of hydrogen. Deuterium possesses a stable nucleus so it is not radioactive, but it weighs twice as much as ordinary hydrogen atoms. By using the mass spectograph —an instrument which can distinguish between ordinary hydrogen and deuterium on the basis of weight—scientists were able to determine how much deuterium was present in a sample.

Shortly after this technique of measuring heavy isotopes became available, Schoenheimer and his co-workers at Columbia University put it to good use. In order to visualize the principles of these experiments let's consider a pool of fat as representing the total amount of fat in the body. We will adjust the conditions of the experiment so that the level of the fat pool remains constant. Fatty acids which are produced by the digestion of fat in our food are carried by the blood and lymph in pipe A in the diagram. If the fat pool is static and is only used as an emergency source of energy (as early investigators believed), then most of the fatty acids in A must go directly to pipe B where they are oxidized to produce energy. Very little of the fatty acids in A would get into the pool.

Another alternative is for the fatty acids in A to go into the pool where they are converted to body fat. Since, under normal conditions, the total body fat remains con-

stant, fat must be drawn off through D to keep the level
of the pool from rising.

In order to decide between these two alternatives, we
must have a way to follow the dietary fatty acids. If this
were a swimming pool instead of a fat pool, we could put
some dye into the water in pipe A. Then after a suitable
period of time we could look at the water in the pool and
see how much dye is in it. If the water from A is passing
into the pool and mixing with it the water in the pool will
be colored. If, on the other hand, the water in A passes
directly into B then the water in the pool will remain un-
colored.

In essence, Schoenheimer carried out this experiment,
but instead of dye he used deuterium atoms. The deuterium was introduced into palmitic acid, a normal fatty
acid. Then this deuterium-labeled palmitic acid was fed
to mice. After four days the mice were killed. The body
fat was isolated and found to contain a large amount of
deuterium. So large amounts of palmitic acid were passing

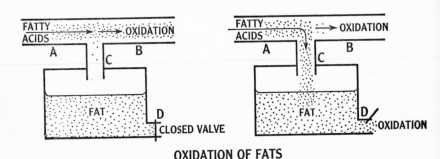

OXIDATION OF FATS

through C into the pool fat. Since the pool remained at the same level an equal amount of pool fat must have been taken off through D and oxidized to yield energy. In fact, Schoenheimer calculated that about half of the pool fat was broken down (through D) and resynthesized (through C) every four days. The fat pool is not static, then, but in a continuous state of flux or *dynamic equilibrium*.

Schoenheimer also made another interesting observation. The largest percentage of deuterium was in the palmitic acid of the pool fat, as expected, but several other fatty acids also contained deuterium. Thus, palmitic acid was not only incorporated into body fat, but it was also converted into other fatty acids. A notable exception was linoleic acid. This unsaturated fatty acid did not contain any deuterium. Thus, palmitic acid cannot be converted to linoleic acid. This confirmed the nutritional studies which had previously established that linoleic acid is an essential fatty acid and therefore must be furnished in the diet since the body cannot make it in sufficient quantities to meet its nutritional needs.

Tracer studies such as these have given us a lot of valuable information about the metabolism of fats and fatty acids. But how are fatty acids oxidized to yield their locked-in energy? And how are fatty acids synthesized in the cells from other sources, such as carbohydrates? These are only samples of the perplexities which biochemists had to unravel in this field.

To answer these questions, biochemists had to study the individual enzymatic reactions involved in the intermediary metabolism of fatty acids. Today we have a fairly good over-all picture of how fatty acids are oxidized to yield energy and the process is strikingly similar to the oxidation of carbohydrates. First the fatty acid molecule is broken into small pieces. In the metabolic dynamo model (Chapter 8) the enzymatic reactions which carry out this process are represented by the water fall. Then these pieces enter the dynamo and are oxidized to carbon dioxide and water by exactly the same reactions which carry out the final oxidation of carbohydrates. And, of course, the energy released in this process is converted to ATP.

The study of the enzymatic reactions involved in carbohydrate and fatty acid metabolism provided the answer to another puzzling observation—the conversion of carbohydrate to fat. As any farmer will tell you, a good, cheap way to fatten animals is to feed them a high carbohydrate diet. Or perhaps you have wondered why you should cut down on carbohydrates as well as fats, if you want to lose weight. The answer is fairly simple.

You will remember that after glycolysis carbohydrates enter the metabolic dynamo for oxidation. But they don't *have* to do this. The body needs a certain amount of carbohydrate to fill its energy requirements. Excess carbohydrate is converted to fat instead of entering the dynamo. This is equivalent to the spillway at a power station. This station has to furnish a certain amount of power and it requires a definite amount of water to turn the turbines which generate this power. When the amount of water behind the dam exceeds the need it spills over. However, the body is much more economical. Instead of wasting the excess energy source it stores it up as fat.

This principle of energy supply and demand is important in controlling body weight. If we eat too much, the supply exceeds the demand and fat is produced. On the other hand, the *only* way one can reduce fat is to make the energy requirements exceed the supply and the best way to achieve this is to eat less. Then the body is forced to call on its fat reserves to meet its energy needs.

Fats are more than just an energy source, however. Just prior to the 'thirties, biochemists found that rats did not grow normally on fat-free diets. When certain types of fats were added to their diet growth was restored to normal, but not all types of fat worked. Eventually the active compounds were identified as unsaturated fatty acids, such as linoleic acid and linolenic acid. The term *essential fatty acids* was coined to describe these fatty acids because they are necessary for normal nutrition.

Man requires unsaturated fatty acids, too. Since the body cannot make them in sufficient quantities to meet its nutritional need, it must obtain them from the food eaten. Yet we don't know what quantity of essential fatty acids is needed or what role they play in metabolism.

Recently, the unsaturated fatty acids have received a

great deal of publicity in connection with arteriosclerosis (hardening of the arteries). Some experiments have suggested that they may help to prevent arteriosclerosis, but this is only a promising lead now. Many more experiments will have to be performed before the final answers are in.

Evidence is also accumulating that fatlike material may be important in other diseases, such as diabetes. So the unglamorous fats are turning out to be important biological materials after all.

10

AMINO ACIDS
THE BUILDING BLOCKS OF PROTEINS

WITHOUT PROTEINS life as we know it would be impossible. Every cell of every living organism contains a variety of proteins with many different functions. Hair and skin are proteins. The membranes surrounding cells contain protein. The metabolic reactions which go on inside the cell are catalyzed by enzymes, which are proteins, and so on.

As far as we know, each cell must make its own proteins; it does this by hooking amino acid building blocks together into long chains which make up the protein molecules. Obviously, a supply of amino acids is necessary. Certain bacteria can make their own amino acids as they need them, but other organisms require them ready-made. Man, for example, is unable to make eight of the twenty amino acids required for protein synthesis. These amino acids must be furnished in the diet. Without them there can be no protein synthesis so they are called *essential amino acids.*

We obtain the essential amino acids by digesting the protein in our food, but not all proteins contain all the essential amino acids. Many years ago, when scientists believed that the nitrogen in proteins was the essential factor, gelatin was served to patients in French hospitals. After all, gelatin contained as much nitrogen as the more expensive meat, milk, and eggs. So why not use this cheap substitute? But the results were disastrous! Invariably, the patients developed severe headaches and nausea. So the diet had to be discontinued, but no one knew why the experiment had failed.

The answer to the gelatin problem didn't come until this century when three American biochemists, Osborne, Mendel, and Rose, clarified the protein-amino acid nutrition story. Osborne had a long-time interest in proteins and through his experiments (as well as those of others) several purified proteins were available. Furthermore, he analyzed the amino acid composition of several purified proteins in some detail so that he knew approximately how much of each amino acid was present in these proteins. In collaboration with Mendel, he fed white rats diets which consisted entirely of purified proteins and followed their growth by weighing them every day. On a purified casein diet the rats grew just as well as control rats did on a normal, mixed diet. However, when *gliadin,* a protein of wheat, or *zein,* a protein of corn, was substituted for casein the rats grew poorly.

Analyses showed that casein was low in glycine, yet the rats grew well on casein. Obviously dietary glycine was not necessary for growth. Gliadin, on the other hand, was deficient in lysine and rats didn't grow well on gliadin. Apparently lysine was necessary for normal growth. If this was true, addition of lysine to the gliadin diet should support normal growth.

Fortunately, pure lysine was available, so Osborne and Mendel could experiment with it. The gliadin diet supplemented with lysine did support growth very well. And so the concept of the essential amino acid was born. According to this concept, the rats could not make lysine in sufficient quantities to meet the requirements of rapid protein synthesis which occurs during growth. So when their diet was deficient in lysine, they failed to grow normally. When lysine was added, protein synthesis was restored to its normal rate and the rats grew. Of course, all twenty of the amino acids are required to make proteins. The distinction between non-essential and essential refers only to whether the organism can make the amino acid or not.

Since the essential amino acids have to be furnished in the diet, it is of considerable practical importance to know which amino acids are essential and how much of each is required for adequate nutrition. William Rose at the University of Illinois set out to solve this problem using a modification of Osborne and Mendel's technique.

Rose decided to feed rats synthetic diets made up of pure amino acids instead of proteins. In this way he could study each amino acid separately to see what effect its omission from the diet would have. This was a very difficult task to put into effect, however. It involved growth studies on twenty different groups of rats on twenty different diets. The rats, because of their inbreeding, were sensitive to even slight changes in their environment, such as noise, temperature changes, even the freshness of their food. And these factors could alter their growth pattern.

To complicate the problem even more, Dr. Rose found that only a few of the amino acids could be purchased commercially and they were very expensive when available. So Rose and his team of graduate students went about the assignment of accumulating amino acids. They made some synthetically in the laboratory and isolated others from mixtures of amino acids obtained from proteins.

When all of the nineteen amino acids known to occur in proteins were fed to rats as their sole source of nitrogen, they failed to grow. In fact, they soon lost weight rapidly. However, if a little casein was added to the amino acid mixture growth commenced. Rose concluded that casein must contain some unknown, essential amino acid. Now to track it down.

First he boiled casein with acid and the resulting amino

acid mixture was subjected to a variety of chemical separations. Each fraction was fed to the rats along with their amino acid diet. One fraction greatly stimulated growth. Closer examination revealed that this fraction contained two amino acids. One of them was already known, *isoleucine.* Finally, the second compound was isolated and it proved to be a brand new amino acid whose presence in proteins had been missed all these years. Rose named it *threonine,* and it was the last of the amino acids which commonly occur in proteins to be discovered.

Now he fed the rats all the previously known amino acids plus threonine. The rats grew well and were healthy. In fact, they grew just as well on this amino acid mixture as they did on casein. This proved conclusively that the amino acids and not proteins *per se* were the important factors. Thus, an old controversy was settled.

The next step involved feeding a group of rats all the amino acids except one, then measuring their growth. Another group was fed a diet lacking another amino acid and so on until the process had been repeated for every possible combination of all the twenty amino acids leaving out one at a time. Ten different groups of rats failed to grow so Rose concluded that the rat requires ten essential amino acids for growth. This little animal can get along without the other ten amino acids in the diet, but leave out any one of the essential ten and the results were invariably the same: First the rat failed to grow, and later, if the missing amino acid was not supplied, it died.

Still Rose was not satisfied. He was convinced that the long, painstaking work had given him conclusive answers for the rat. But what about human beings? What are their needs? He decided that it wasn't practical to use growth as the measurement criterion because no one would want his children to be subjected to deficient growth conditions. No, children couldn't be used. Moreover, he wanted to get information about amino acid requirements on adults where the growth pattern would not be a useful measure anyway. So he turned to *nitrogen balance* studies.

From the nineteenth century experiments of the German physiologist Carl Voit, Rose knew that a normal human subject on a nutritionally adequate diet excreted the same amount of nitrogen in his urine and feces as he took in as food. The subject was said to be in nitrogen balance. However, when an essential amino acid was omitted from the diet, the subject went into negative nitrogen balance, that is, he excreted more nitrogen than he took in. Using nitrogen balance as a test, Rose established that there are eight essential amino acids for adults. Included in this list are tryptophan, phenylalanine and lysine, all of which are missing from gelatin. Thus, gelatin is an imperfect protein from a nutritional point of view and cannot meet the body's needs by itself. At last the failure of gelatin to replace the mixed proteins found in milk, meat, and eggs was understood. This explained why the sick Frenchmen had those aggravating headaches and nausea when fed gelatin as a source of protein in their hospital diets. Now we know that adults need about seventy grams of *mixed* proteins in the daily diet in order to ensure an adequate supply of the essential amino acids. In addition this protein acts as a nitrogen source for synthesis of the other amino acids.

As the nutritional aspects of the protein-amino acid story unfolded, many biochemists became interested in how proteins are built up and broken down in the body. One of the first questions which had to be answered was, "Are the body proteins stable or are they being built up and broken down continuously?" We can use the pool analogy which we applied to fats (Chapter 9) to illustrate this point. When the diet is nutritionally adequate, the body is in nitrogen balance. This means the nitrogen going into pipe A as amino acids must equal the nitrogen

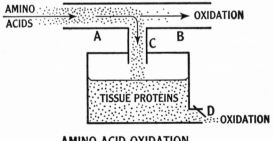

AMINO ACID OXIDATION

waste products coming out of the body as products of oxidation (pipe B or D). It also means that the size of the tissue protein pool does not change under these conditions. Now we want to know whether the dietary amino acids (pipe A) are oxidized directly without entering the pool (A to B) or do they enter the pool through C before being oxidized (pipe D)? This was a job for isotopic tracers.

Rudolf Schoenheimer and his associates at Columbia University prepared amino acids containing a heavy, stable isotope of nitrogen (N^{15}) which can be distinguished from ordinary nitrogen with a mass spectrograph. Schoenheimer fed these labeled amino acids to rats and analyzed their excreta and tissues for N^{15}. The tissue protein contained about 28 per cent of the total isotope. This could only mean that a significant amount of the dietary amino acids enter the protein pool through C. Since the pool size was constant, some of the tissue protein had to be broken down to amino acids which were piped off through D and oxidized. Thus, proteins, like fats and carbohydrates, are in a state of dynamic equilibrium in which the protein molecules are broken down and rapidly resynthesized.

The tissue proteins represent an emergency energy source since the amino acids produced by protein breakdown can be oxidized in much the same way as fatty acids or sugars. In fact, removal of nitrogen converts amino acids to compounds which are very close chemical relatives of the fatty acids. These *keto acids* are oxidized by the metabolic dynamo to give carbon dioxide, water, and energy. So you see, oxidation of all the food types is very similar.

The nitrogen which is removed from the amino acids during metabolism presents a special problem. The body can't oxidize it and so it must get rid of it. To make matters worse, the nitrogen is actually removed from amino acids as ammonia which is very poisonous to most cells. This ammonia must be quickly removed from the body or converted to a less toxic substance. In most mammals, including man, the ammonia is converted to a relatively nontoxic substance called *urea*. The urea is excreted in the urine and represents the nitrogen from oxidized amino acids.

Urea formation occurs primarily in the liver. This can be demonstrated in several ways. If the liver is removed from a dog, for example, it can survive for several days if *all* proteins (or amino acids) are withheld from the diet. As soon as proteins (or amino acids) are fed, however, the dog quickly dies. When the blood and urine are analyzed, large amounts of ammonia and very little urea are found. In a normal animal the reverse is true—the blood and urine contain urea, but very little ammonia. Thus, the liver must be important in the conversion of ammonia to urea.

If a liver is carefully removed from an animal, the conversion of ammonia to urea can be demonstrated by *per-*

fusion experiments. The liver is placed in a closed system so that various fluids can be pumped through it continuously in the same way that blood is pumped through it under normal conditions. When a solution containing either ammonia or amino acids is perfused through the liver ammonia disappears and urea appears in the fluid emerging from the organ.

Although a great deal has been learned about the breakdown (catabolism) of proteins and amino acids over the years, the problem of protein synthesis in living organisms remains one of the most frustrating problems in modern biochemistry.

As early as the latter part of the nineteenth century it was known that proteins are broken down to amino acids by the addition of water to the peptide bonds which hold them together. Furthermore, many enzymes, such as pepsin and trypsin, which catalyzed these hydrolytic reactions were known to occur in the body; this led to the idea that proteins were synthesized simply by reversing the process of digestion.

There was some evidence to support this, but theoretical considerations soon made it clear that a considerable amount of energy was required to put a protein together again once it had been hydrolyzed to its amino acids. Thus, a simple reversal of hydrolysis seemed most unlikely. The explanation of protein synthesis turned toward an inclusion of a process in which the amino acids are activated so they can hook together to form a protein chain. Recent experiments suggest how this may take place but there are still many puzzling discrepancies.

The activation step in protein synthesis is probably the simplest part of the problem. It is reasonably certain that each individual type of protein has a specific sequence of amino acids. Thus, the enzyme trypsin may have the sequence A-B-C-D—et cetera, while the enzyme pepsin may have the sequence D-B-C-A—et cetera. Even the simplest protein is composed of peptide chains containing thirty or more amino acid residues and many proteins appear to contain several hundred amino acids. There is an almost infinite number of ways in which these residues could be linked together. Consequently, hooking together activated amino acids to give a specific protein with a specific function can't be a random process.

The body must have some ingenious scheme for placing the right amino acids in the right place in the protein molecule. So far there is little concrete evidence to support the theories of how this may occur, and the task is complicated because of our limited knowledge about the sequence of amino acids in a specific protein. We will have to learn more about protein structure to solve this enigma.

Even solving the sequence of amino acids will not complete the task. What about the specific shape of the protein molecule? Some proteins, such as the globulins, form more or less spherical molecules; other molecules are rod-shaped. So the final answer will have to include how the peptide chain is coiled up to form the finished protein molecule.

Recent progress has been made by taking pictures of crystalline proteins with X-rays. These pictures don't yield the well-defined shapes that are obtained when the body is X-rayed but instead give a collection of spots of different intensities. These spots represent different atoms within the molecule. However, in a structure as complicated as a protein, it is extremely difficult to translate this information into a chemical structure. Progress is inching along. For example, Linus Pauling, a recent Nobel Prize winner for his work on proteins, and his co-workers have interpreted X-ray data from certain proteins, notably keratin—a protein found in hair and skin —to indicate that these protein molecules are *helical*— that is, they are coiled like a spring. However, it is clear that we are a long way from a clear understanding of protein structure and how this takes place in the body.

Perhaps one of the reasons biochemists are so interested in the relationship between protein structure and biological function is that proteins play so many different roles in the body. The most important function of proteins, as we have seen, is as enzymes. But they have other functions as well. The respiratory protein *hemoglobin* is a good example. Without hemoglobin we cannot live. The red cells are packed with it and when the blood passes through the lungs, it picks up the oxygen we breathe. The oxygen combines with the hemoglobin and gets a piggy-back ride to the various cells of the body where it is released to carry out the oxidation reactions of the cells. If a person is exposed to carbon monoxide, this gas combines with the hemoglobin. In fact, it combines so strongly that oxygen is displaced from the hemoglobin. Since carbon monoxide can't replace oxygen in oxidative metabolism, the cells are deprived of their normal oxygen supply and are unable to carry out the respiratory reactions which are necessary for normal cell function. The end result, of course, is death.

Another important nonenzymatic function of proteins has to do with our resistance to infection. When complex foreign substances such as bacteria or viruses enter the blood, the body mobilizes its defenses to get rid of them. One defense mechanism is the formation of *antibodies*. As yet we don't know how the body makes antibodies, but we do know that they combine with the foreign substances which provoke their formation, the *antigen,* and render it harmless.

Antibodies are something of a puzzle, too. They are proteins found in the gamma globulin fraction of blood serum. They appear to be specific for the antigen which triggered their formation. Thus, there is a specific antibody for each strain of polio virus which has no effect on the other two strains.

The antigen doesn't have to be a living organism. Any complex substance, dead bacteria, proteins, and even carbohydrates which are foreign to the organism, can elicit antibody formation. One of the interesting features of antibody formation is that in many instances once antibodies are formed in the body they may be maintained at a high level, or *titer,* as it is called, for many years. Yet, in some cases, antibody titer drops rapidly after the antigen disappears. Thus, usually we have resistance for the rest of our lives to many of the so-called childhood diseases, such as chicken pox, measles, and whooping cough, once we have had the disease. But in the case of some infections, such as the common cold, resistance is transitory and having a cold is no insurance that another won't follow in short order.

Certain hormones are proteins, too. For example, insulin is a protein molecule which plays a role in the regulation of both carbohydrate and fat metabolism in the body. When the pancreas loses its ability to produce insulin, the metabolic machinery gets out of adjustment and diabetes results. Naturally a great deal of interest has centered on the role of insulin in metabolic control, but as yet we lack the complete answer to some of these important questions.

One of the greatest advances in protein chemistry has come from the brilliant work of Fred Sanger, England's 1958 Nobel Prize winner in chemistry. For over ten years he and his colleagues methodically pursued the amino acid sequence in the insulin molecule until at last they were able to put this giant jigsaw puzzle together with every piece in its right place.

Because of Sanger's work we now know that insulin is composed of two chains of amino acids lying side by side. And the amino acid sequence of both chains is known! Sanger's remarkable achievement gave the biochemist new methods and new confidence in attacking the problem of protein structure. With rapid progress now being made in laboratories in many countries, no doubt the baffling questions about the relationship between protein structure and biological activity will soon be answered.

11

HORMONES
CHEMICAL REGULATORS

ALL OF US have had "butterflies" in our stomachs at one time or another before some important event in our lives, such as making a speech before a large audience or taking an examination. Butterflies are caused by the action of *adrenalin,* a chemical which belongs to an elite group of substances called hormones.

When the body is confronted with a situation which requires a greater than normal effort, either physical or mental, two small glands, the adrenals which are located on top of the kidneys, begin to pour adrenalin into the blood. As the blood circulates it carries the hormone to the tissues of the body where it initiates a series of remarkable changes, such as an increase in output of blood by the heart, an increase in output of glucose by the liver, and the inhibition of stomach muscle contraction. These and many other changes which prepare the body for emergency action cause the sensation which we call butterflies.

The body contains about three dozen different hormones which regulate the metabolic reactions of the cells. The result of the particular control which a certain hormone exerts appears as some observable phenomenon. For example, adrenalin stimulates the release of energy-yielding glucose. This means that the muscles are able to contract much longer than usual because their source of energy has been increased. In part, this explains the almost superhuman efforts, such as the four-minute mile, which are possible under emergency conditions. Other hormones have different effects: thyroxine, the thyroid hormone, speeds up the oxidative metabolism of the body; estrogens, the female sex hormones, are important in the reproductive cycle, and so on.

Chemically, the hormones are very different too, ranging in complexity from simple molecules, such as adrenalin, to complicated proteins, such as growth hormone. However, the unique property which distinguishes hormones as a group from other body chemicals is their secretion directly into the blood by the so-called endocrine glands. Then they are carried by the circulatory system to the cells of the body where they exert their particular action.

The discovery of hormones came during studies aimed at finding out how the body controls the flow of digestive juices. Before 1900, it was known that digestive juices are not poured into the stomach and intestines continuously. Instead, their flow is stimulated by the presence of food. Most scientists of that day believed that this was controlled entirely by the nervous system.

However, a curious report appeared in the literature which claimed that hydrochloric acid (a normal component of gastric juice) placed in the intestine of an experimental animal stimulated the flow of digestive juices from the pancreas. Furthermore, this stimulation of pancreatic secretion continued even after the main nerves leading to the pancreas had been cut.

Such a radical suggestion could not go unchallenged, and Bayliss and Starling, two English physiologists, decided to check it. In 1902, they performed the now classical experiment which revolutionized physiological thinking.

These physiologists anesthetized a dog and then carefully opened its abdomen, exposing a loop of small intestine. They cut all the nerves leading to the intestinal loop as well as those leading to the pancreas, but they left the blood supply to these organs intact. Thus the only contact between the pancreas and the intestinal loop was through the blood. Next, a special needle (a canula) was inserted into the pancreatic duct, which carries the pancreatic juice to the intestine, and the canula was attached to a recording device in order to follow the flow of pancreatic juice accurately.

When hydrochloric acid was introduced into the intestinal loop, secretion of pancreatic juice began. Since the nerves had been severed, the stimulation must have been carried by some other means. According to an observer present at the experiment Starling exclaimed, "Then it must be a chemical reflex!"

The next step was obvious to the experimenters. They cut out the intestinal loop and ground it up with sand to break up the cells. They filtered the mixture to remove the debris and injected the clear filtrate into a vein. After about seventy seconds, the pancreatic juice began to flow and almost twice as fast as before. Clearly the intestinal tract contained some chemical agent which was carried by the blood to the pancreas where it stimulated the flow of pancreatic juice. Bayliss and Starling named this substance *secretin*.

The results of this experiment soon reached the great Russian physiologist Pavlov, one of the leading investigators in gastronintestinal physiology. Pavlov was convinced from his own work that all the secretions of the digestive juices were caused by impulses traveling along nerves.

Since the result of the Englishmen's work was contrary to this belief, Pavlov asked one of his assistants to repeat the experiment. An eyewitness described the incident: "The effect of secretin was self-evident. Pavlov and the rest of us watched the experiment in silence. Then, without a word, Pavlov disappeared into his study.

He returned a half hour later and said, 'Of course, they are right. It is clear that we did not take out the exclusive patent for the discovery of the truth.' "

Bayliss and Starling suggested that the name *hormone* should be used to describe compounds like secretin which are secreted by some tissue directly into the blood which then carries it to some other tissue where it exerts its physiological action. Their definition even suggested how one might go about finding new hormones: Remove some tissue, prepare an extract, inject it, and see what happens.

Progress was rapid in learning about hormones as scientists in all parts of the world turned their attention to this field. As new hormones were discovered, scientists began to realize that many hormones are secreted by endocrine glands. These special glands, as the name implies, have no tubes or ducts connecting them with other tissues of the body. In this respect they differ from ordinary glands, such as the salivary glands, whose secretions are carried to specific places in the body by tiny tubes. The endocrine glands, on the other hand, are well supplied with blood vessels which pick up the hormones and distribute them throughout the body.

Today several endocrine glands whose only function is to manufacture and secrete hormones have been found. The pituitary (a small pea-shaped gland at the base of the brain), the thyroid (the shield-shaped gland in the neck), the parathyroids (imbedded in the thyroid tissue) and the adrenals (on top of the kidneys) are endocrine glands of this type. Some hormones, however, are produced by tissues which perform other important physiological functions. In this respect, the stomach, the small intestine, the pancreas, the ovaries, and the testes are endocrine glands.

ENDOCRINE GLANDS

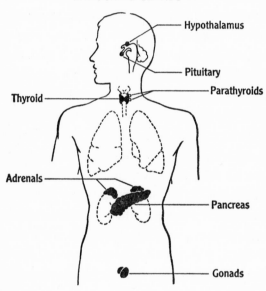

The main function of hormones appears to be the regulation of cell metabolism. As we have seen, a cell is a complicated chemical machine and, like any other machine, it must be carefully adjusted if it is to operate efficiently. Even in single-celled organisms, such as bacteria, this control mechanism is a complicated process which scientists understand only partially. And in multicellular organisms, such as man, the process is even more complicated. Each cell is still a separate chemical unit, but now many cells must function together to produce an efficient organism. Thus, the body must have some way to control the function of various organs so that they work as a team under a wide variety of conditions. The hormones, at least in part, provide this control.

As an example of this hormonal control of metabolism, consider the regulation of blood sugar. Under normal conditions the amount of glucose in the blood remains remarkably constant, even though the amount in the diet varies considerably. To understand how the body does this we can think of the liver as a factory where each liver cell is a workshop and the liver enzymes are the workers. The liver factory must supply enough glucose to meet the demands of the consumers, such as brain and muscle. The circulatory system provides transportation for bringing glucose from the food to the liver and for carrying it from the liver to other tissues. Hence, under normal conditions the supply equals the demand, and the blood sugar stays constant.

When we eat a high carbohydrate meal, the supply of glucose exceeds the demand, but the blood level still remains the same. It is carried by the blood to the liver where it is converted to glycogen, a storage form of glucose. In principle this is like the manufacturing company that builds up an inventory of its products. If we fast for several hours, all of our food has been digested and absorbed. The supply of glucose is zero, yet the blood sugar remains constant. Now the demand for glucose exceeds the supply so the liver enzymes go to work again, but this time they bring glycogen out of the warehouse and convert it to glucose. This sugar is picked up by the blood leaving the liver and is carried to the other tissues.

Of course, the supply of glucose from glycogen can't go on indefinitely. In fact, the glycogen stores would be exhausted in less than a day if this were the only source of glucose. Fortunately, the body has another major depot, the proteins. When necessary, tissue proteins can be converted to amino acids which are carried to the liver by the blood and there turned into glucose and glycogen by the liver enzymes.

We can summarize these facts by the following diagram:

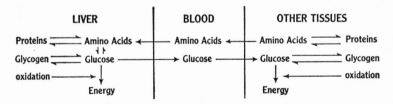

Now the problem is: How does the body control this maze of reactions? How do the enzyme workers know what to do? How do they know when the blood sugar is dropping—or rising? How do they know that the glycogen stores are low or exhausted? How do they know when to build up tissue proteins and when to break them down to supply amino acids for glucose production? Again, scientists still haven't given us the complete answers, but we do know that hormones play an important role in regulating these metabolic reactions.

One of the most famous hormones, insulin, is required for this metabolic scheme to function normally. When the beta cells of the pancreas fail to produce enough insulin, the blood sugar begins to rise, and eventually, when it reaches a sufficiently high level, it begins to appear in the urine (glucosuria). This is one of the symptoms of the metabolic disease known as diabetes. But the diabetic has many other metabolic troubles: fat is not oxidized properly, glycogen stores in the liver and muscles are low, and so on. When insulin is injected into a diabetic, the messed-up metabolic reactions begin to return to normal. The liver and muscles begin to build up glycogen; the blood sugar drops and glucosuria disappears; fat metabolism returns to normal, and so on.

Of course, the big question is: How does insulin accomplish these remarkable feats? As yet, we lack the complete answer. We do know that insulin affects not only the uptake of glucose from the blood by the muscles, but also the release of sugar into the blood by the liver. In muscle, insulin appears to aid penetration of glucose from the blood into the muscle cells. The role of insulin in the liver is apparently much more complicated. It's a tough problem, but the pieces are slowly fitting together.

Insulin is not the only hormone that regulates carbohydrate metabolism. Adrenalin also plays an important role, particularly under emergency conditions when an all-out effort is required. Under such conditions, a large expenditure of energy may be necessary and hence an increased supply of glucose will be needed. When such a condition arises, the central control station, the brain, signals the adrenal glands by a nerve impulse which stimulates the release of adrenalin. This is equivalent to picking up the telephone and ordering, "Adrenalin, quick!" The blood picks up the hormone and carries it to the liver where it stimulates the breakdown of glycogen and the production of glucose. Apparently, it accomplishes this by increasing the activity of one of the liver enzymes which is responsible for glycogen breakdown.

Adrenalin is carried by the blood to other tissues, too. One of these is the pituitary gland, and when the adrenalin arrives it says, in effect, "I need help in rounding up more glucose. The muscles are using it up faster than the factory can produce it."

The pituitary responds to adrenalin stimulation by releasing a second hormone, *adrenocorticotropic hormone* (ACTH), which exerts its action on the adrenal gland. So adrenalin is really sending this messenger

(ACTH) back home (to the adrenals) for help. When ACTH reaches the adrenals, it stimulates the release of a group of hormones called the *adrenal cortical steroids,* which includes such famous substances as *cortisone.* These hormones stimulate the conversion of tissue proteins to amino acids which are carried to the liver where they are converted to glucose and glycogen.

Thus, adrenalin not only mobilizes the body's glycogen stores for immediate action, but it also signals reinforcements by triggering the release of ACTH which ultimately leads to the conversion of proteins to glucose. Complicated? Yes, but you will have to agree it is a pretty neat system. Of course this brief explanation leaves many unanswered questions, but perhaps the example has served to illustrate the complexity of hormonal control as well as the importance of these chemical regulators.

The knowledge gained from the study of hormones and endocrine glands (endocrinology) has provided the foundation for some very important medical applications. Before the turn of this century several diseases were associated with the absence or degeneration of tissues which are now known to be endocrine glands. Take myxedema (Gull's disease); it was associated with the absence or destruction of the thyroid gland. In fact, the endocrine nature of the thyroid was actually demonstrated in 1891. An English physician named Murray took one of his patients who was suffering from myxedema to the local medical society and asked his colleagues to confirm his diagnosis. Then he obtained some fresh thyroid tissue from the local slaughterhouse and extracted it with glycerin. After injection of the extract, the patient amazed the doctors at the medical society with her miraculous recovery. This was one of the first experiments in clinical endocrinology, but the idea that the thyroid was actually a gland which secreted a chemical substance into the blood was not appreciated until after Bayliss and Starling accomplished their brilliant experiment.

Other diseases were also related to the endocrine glands. Examination of patients who had died of Addison's disease revealed that the adrenal glands had degenerated. Removal of the pancreas from experimental dogs led to a disease which was almost identical to diabetes in humans, and so on.

Today many of the endocrine diseases are cured or at least controlled by the administration of extracts of the appropriate gland, and in some cases a pure hormone can be used in treatment. For example, a person with an underactive thyroid may be given doses of the pure thyroid hormone, thyroxine. Cortisone, an adrenal cortical hormone, was one of the first agents to be used successfully against arthritis.

Today pituitary extracts are often given to children who are not growing normally. In such cases the pituitary gland is not functioning normally and is not secreting enough growth hormone.

Oxytocin, another pituitary hormone, is sometimes used to induce labor in pregnant women.

Diabetes can be controlled by the injection of pure insulin.

Indeed, the list of medical uses for the hormones is a long and important one in modern practice.

As a result of hundreds of experiments which have been performed since the turn of the century, we are able to describe the physiological function of the various glands in considerable detail. We know which hormones they secrete and the chemical nature of these hormones. We also know what happens when the gland is missing or when it ceases to function normally, and in many cases we know how to correct the situation. We even know what effect various pure hormones have upon the cells of the body.

Yet with all this progress we still don't know how hormones act. For example, we know that thyroxine stimulates the oxidation of foodstuffs, but we don't know how it brings this about. We also know that the pituitary hormone ACTH stimulates the production of several steroid hormones by the adrenal glands. But we don't know how ACTH alters the metabolism of the adrenals so that they make more of these hormones available. This is the type of puzzle which biochemists interested in hormones are trying to solve today.

12

VITAMINS LEND A HAND

MOST OF US take vitamins pretty much for granted. Usually, we get an adequate supply in our food or by taking vitamin pills so we don't think much about these important substances. Yet we cannot survive without vitamins for they are involved either directly or indirectly in almost every process the body carries out.

Every day in the food we eat we consume large amounts of carbohydrate, protein, and fat to furnish energy and cellular building materials. But all this food does us very little good if our diet doesn't include a supply of many different vitamins, because without them, our cells can't oxidize the foodstuffs to provide energy. And without energy, we can't make new cellular materials or move our muscles, and so on. Yet an entire day's supply of vitamins can be crammed into a pill no larger than a pea.

Scientists still do not understand the function of all the vitamins, but many of them form enzyme helpers. Many enzymes, particularly those involved in oxidation reactions, require a *coenzyme* in order to function. The coenzymes are relatively small molecules which are attached to the large protein part of the enzyme. The coenzyme is actually responsible for carrying out the reaction. If we think of a machine which punches holes in a metal sheet, the coenzyme is like the punch itself while the enzyme is represented by the rest of the machine. However, any one coenzyme will act *by itself* with many different substances. The body controls which substance it will actually react with by combining it with a specific protein molecule. The protein selects the proper compound, and the coenzyme carries out the reaction. The result of this team work is a highly specific enzyme.

Many of the B vitamins are used by the body to make coenzymes. Vitamin B_2 (riboflavin), for example, is required to make coenzyme I, which plays an important role in a large number of oxidation reactions. Actually, the vitamins are not really any different than other essential nutritional materials which we have encountered. Essential amino acids, for example, are required for the synthesis of protein just as certain vitamins are required to make certain coenzymes. The only striking difference between them lies in the amounts required, but even this is easily understandable. The body has to manufacture large quantities of protein and, accordingly, relatively large amounts of essential amino acids are required. But only small amounts of coenzymes are needed and so only small amounts of the vitamins are required.

Not all organisms require vitamins. Some bacteria, but not all, have no vitamin requirements. They will thrive on a diet of simple salts and an energy source, such as glucose. Yet they need the same coenzymes as man. The difference lies in the fact that these bacteria can make their own coenzymes from very simple building blocks supplied by the salts and glucose. Other organisms, through evolution, have lost this ability to use very simple building materials. Man, for example, obtained adequate quantities of these essential substances in his food and so lost his ability to make them from simpler materials.

Vitamin research has established that more than a dozen of these essential factors are required for humans. Furthermore, the body cannot store some of these substances so they must be furnished each day. If any one is lacking from the diet for very long, the body's normal function is impaired and a vitamin deficiency disease results. Today, in America, with an abundance of fresh foods and vitamin supplements, these diseases are not very common. But not long ago they represented a very serious health problem.

Deficiency diseases appear to date to our earliest record of man. Some skeletons of prehistoric man show definite signs of *scurvy* (vitamin C deficiency) and *beriberi* (vitamin B_1 deficiency). Ancient Egyptian papyri describe treatment of travelers who had developed eyesight disorders (vitamin A deficiency) after long periods of exposure in the desert. Priests chose favorable omens and, with suitable incantations, fed the sufferers the liver (a good source of vitamin A) of a donkey sacrificed for the occasion.

Slowly men came to realize that there was a definite relationship between diet and certain disease states and that the human diet must contain more than carbohydrate, fat, and protein in the interest of good health. By trial and error they learned to cure many of these deficiency diseases without understanding their causes or the nature of the curative agents.

Consider scurvy as an example. It was a dreaded disease both in ancient and modern times. Usually it appeared when there was a lack of food, particularly fresh fruits and vegetables, as in time of war, on long voyages, or during famines. The Crusaders were plagued by it on their journeys to the Holy Land; thousands of soldiers died of it in the Crimean War; and it is said that as many as 15 per cent of the deaths in our own Civil War were caused by it. Vasco da Gama lost 100 of his 160-man crew from scurvy on his Cape of Good Hope expedition. Other explorers reported similar disasters. Of course this was at a time when the diet of sailors at sea consisted in the main of salt pork and hard biscuits. It was long before the time of refrigeration and fresh foods for seagoing crews.

A real breakthrough in the treatment of scurvy came in 1701 when Captain James Lancaster introduced the use of lemon juice aboard his ship the *General* on a voyage from England to the East Indies. The results were amazing. His crew stayed well for the entire voyage while the crews on companion ships suffered many cases of scurvy.

Today we know that scurvy is caused by a deficiency of vitamin C (ascorbic acid) and that the juice from citrus fruits is a rich source of this vitamin. Thus, Lancaster had empirically found a cure for scurvy which today is on sound scientific footing. Yet even today biochemists are not sure what role ascorbic acid plays in the body's metabolism or how a deficiency of this vitamin leads to scurvy.

Another vitamin deficiency disease which plagued man for centuries was rickets. First described in 1650, it manifests its symptoms most clearly in children. It is characterized by skeletal deformities, such as bow legs and knock-knees; abnormal formation of teeth; generally retarded growth; and lack of vigor. This syndrome is a manifestation of an abnormal metabolism of calcium and phosphate.

In 1822, almost 200 years after rickets was first described as a disease, cod liver oil as well as sunlight were suggested as cures. Unfortunately, men paid little heed to the suggestions and rickets raged on for many more years. In fact, the disease was so common that in the large cities of Europe and America most of the children displayed symptoms of rickets.

Now we know that rickets is caused by a deficiency

of vitamin D. Fish liver oils are a rich source of this vitamin and the curative effects of sunlight are on sure footing too. Vitamin D exists in an inactive (*provitamin*) form which is converted to the active vitamin by irradiation of the provitamin with sunlight. In fact, many of our foods, such as milk, are enriched in active vitamin D by irradiation with artificial sunlight.

By the turn of the century, it was quite clear that many diseases were closely related to diet, but the nature of the essential dietary factors was still a mystery. Sir Frederick Gowland Hopkins, a famous British biochemist, Nobel Prize winner, and one-time President of the Royal Society, summed up the situation in 1906: "No animal can live upon a mixture of pure protein, fat and carbohydrate, and even when inorganic material is carefully supplied, the animal still cannot flourish. The animal body is adjusted to live either upon plant tissues or other animals and these contain countless substances other than proteins, carbohydrates and fats. Physiological evolution, I believe, has made some of these well nigh as essential as are the basic constituents of the diet. . . . In diseases such as rickets, and particularly scurvy, we have had long years of knowledge of the dietetic factor; but though we know how to benefit these conditions empirically, the real errors in the diet are to this day quite obscure."

One of the early break-throughs in understanding the nature of vitamins came from experiments performed in a Javanese penal colony by a Dutch army surgeon named Christiaan Eijkman. He was the first person to produce a dietary deficiency disease experimentally. He noticed that when chickens were fed a diet of only polished rice —the staple of the natives—they sickened with a strange disease called polyneuritis. This was similar to the human deficiency disease known as beriberi which had plagued the peoples of the Orient for centuries. First the chicks became weak, then paralyzed, and soon died. Dr. Eijkman found he could revive some of them by feeding them the brown outer husks of rice (pericarps or "silver skins") which were considered unfit for human consumption and so were usually discarded.

This was a monumental discovery. Its importance was not that Eijkman demonstrated the curative effect of a specific food on a deficiency disease, for this had been demonstrated many times, but rather that this was the first instance where a deficiency disease was produced and cured by restoring the same food in *experimental animals*. This was of tremendous significance because it pointed to the fact that organisms other than man suffer from deficiency diseases and might be used to good advantage to unravel the mystery of such conditions in man. Thus, the use of experimental chickens provided assay procedures which were necessary for the isolation of the chemical substance responsible for the curative effect. Without this assay looking for accessory factors was like looking for a needle in a haystack. However, with an assay to act as a magnet there was a much better chance of picking out the needle.

Eijkman believed that those brown outer husks contained an elixirlike substance essential to health. Perhaps in the absence of this substance the utilization of sugar follows an abnormal path in the body. The answers were slow in coming and the world had to wait thirty years before Eijkman's insight into the role of "vitamines" could be confirmed.

In 1911, Casimir Funk, a Bern-educated biochemist, produced polyneuritis in chickens at Lister Institute of Preventive Medicine in London. He fed the experimental chickens polished rice and induced sickness in them, then cured them by feeding them rice bran (the outer husk removed during the polishing process). Then Funk extracted rice bran with dilute acid and obtained an impure substance which cured and prevented polyneuritis in chickens and beriberi in man.

Since this material was a mixture of several chemical substances, Funk was unable to find out much about the chemical nature of the polyneuritis-curing substance, but concluded that it was an *amine* (a particular class of organic compounds). Since this amine was essential for life, Funk coined the word *vitamine* (*vita,* from the Latin *vita,* life + English *amine*). Soon other accessory factors were discovered and, since they were not all amines, the word *vitamin* was adopted to avoid having any chemical meaning attached to the name.

Funk's discovery stimulated one of the most intensive searches in biochemical history. Biochemists all over the world took up the hunt for the antipolyneuritis factor, or "water-soluble B," as it was often called because it could be extracted from various foods with water. Soon it became apparent that water soluble B was not a single vitamin. For example, Smith and Hendrick found that when rats were fed a diet of oats, protein, calcium, and butterfat the animals did not grow well. When yeast (known to be a good source of water-soluble vitamin B) was added they grew much better. To be sure of their results, Smith and Hendrick heated the yeast to inactivate the vitamin. To their surprise, the rats continued to grow well when the heated yeast was added to the deficient diet. It was well established, however, that the antineuritic factor was destroyed by heat so they concluded that yeast contained a second vitamin which helped to promote growth.

Thus, the belief was held that water-soluble B contained two vitamins, one which prevented or cured polyneuritis in fowl and beriberi in man and a second which promoted growth and well-being in rats.

Finally, in 1926, a pure, crystalline substance which was extremely active in curing polyneuritis in pigeons was isolated. Since this was the first B vitamin to be isolated in pure form it was named vitamin B_1. Later, when its chemical structure had been determined it was named *thiamine.*

By a series of developments similar to those which have just been described, the second vitamin, vitamin B_2 or riboflavin, was isolated. Other water-soluble vitamins were isolated in rapid succession.

With the discovery of riboflavin and nicotinic acid (niacin), which soon followed, the pattern was established. First, observations were made on experimental animals which developed certain characteristic symptoms when they were kept on a certain type of deficient diet. Secondly, an extract of some foodstuff (often yeast or liver) was found to cure the symptoms of the disease. Finally, attempts were made to purify the factor by using the deficiency disease as an assay to follow the various purification steps.

So several different B vitamins came from water-soluble B, which at first was thought to be a single vitamin. These substances were grouped together for historical reasons and became known as the B-complex vitamins. Chemically, they are unrelated but they do have two properties in common: All of them are water soluble and act as enzyme helpers (coenzymes).

Today seven B-vitamins are known to be important in human nutrition: Thiamin (B_1), riboflavin (B_2), nicotinic acid (niacin), pyridoxine (B_6), pantothenic acid, folic acid, and vitamin B_{12} and others are suspected.

The B vitamins and vitamin C compose the group referred to as the water-soluble vitamins. However, a second group, the fat-soluble vitamins, is equally important. This group, which is insoluble in water, but soluble in organic solvents, includes vitamins A, D, E, and K. A and D were discovered about the same time as water-soluble B as a result of attempts to explain the curative effect of certain fatlike substances (for example, fish liver oil) on certain deficiency diseases.

During the years 1913 to 1915, two groups of workers in this country—McCollum and his co-workers at the University of Wisconsin and Osborne and Mendel at Yale—found that when rats were fed a diet in which purified lard or olive oil was used as a source of fat, the animals failed to grow. However, when butterfat, cod liver oil, or egg yolk was substituted for the lard or olive oil, normal growth resumed and the appearance of the animals improved markedly. McCollum designated the active principle which was present in these fats as fat-soluble A. This material differed from vitamin B in that it was not extractable with water and had no antineuritic activity.

The recognition of fat-soluble A and its distinction from water-soluble B touched off a wave of interest in the occurrence and nature of this vitamin. Cod liver oil was a particularly rich source of fat-soluble A and at once the possible role of this substance in preventing and curing diseases such as rickets was recognized.

In 1919, Edward Mellanby delivered two lectures to the Royal College of Surgeons in London on the cause of rickets. He described how he produced rickets in dogs;

he found that he could cure them by adding fats such as cod liver oil or butter to the deficient diets. He modified the diets and found that the faster the dogs grew the more easily rickets developed and the harder it was to stop its course. He concluded that many animal and vegetable fats prevented rickets, but some, such as linseed oil, did not. "An examination of the results obtained suggests that rickets is a deficiency disease which develops in consequence of the absence of some accessory factor or factors."

Of the three known vitamins at this time—A, B, and C—water-soluble vitamin B and antiscorbutic vitamin C could be ruled out because yeast (water-soluble B) and orange juice (vitamin C) had no effect in preventing rickets. Mellanby decided that the probable cause of rickets is a diminished intake of an antirachitic factor which is either fat-soluble A or has a somewhat similar distribution to fat-soluble A.

There were some discrepancies, however, in Mellanby's experiments. One of the most puzzling observations was that rickets developed best in rapidly growing animals. This was in accord with clinical observation that large and rapidly growing children suffered from rickets while sickly children generally escaped the disease. This was hard to reconcile with the known fact that fat-soluble A stimulated growth. Thus, a deficiency in fat-soluble A should inhibit growth—precisely the reverse of conditions Mellanby had found to be most conducive to rickets.

Finally, in 1922 McCollum showed that fat-soluble A was a mixture of at least two substances: One (vitamin A) cured xerophthalmia, an inflammatory eye disease, and stimulated growth in rats; the second (vitamin D) prevented and cured rickets. These vitamins were soon isolated in pure form and their chemical structure determined. Other fat-soluble vitamins were rapidly discovered: vitamin E, the antisterility factor, and vitamin K, the antihemorrhagic factor, among them.

Thus, a new class of biologically important substances, vitamins, was clearly established. Today the function of most of the B vitamins is clearly understood. As we pointed out earlier, they form coenzymes. Riboflavin is an integral part of many of the coenzymes which link the oxidation of foodstuffs to oxygen. Nicotinic acid-containing coenzymes are important in oxidation reactions also. Pyridoxine functions as a coenzyme in amino acid metabolism and so on.

Our knowledge of the function of the fat-soluble vitamins is much less complete. Their most detailed story concerns the function of vitamin A which has been worked out by Dr. George Wald at Harvard University. Our ability to see at night is dependent upon vitamin A and Wald and his associates have been able to explain how the vitamin functions in this process. But we know almost nothing about how vitamins D or E work, and we only have a promising hint of the role of vitamin K.

So the struggle to understand the complex machinery

which goes on within the living organism continues. Vitamin research has contributed a great deal to our understanding of these fundamental processes, and, of course, there have been many practical applications of this knowledge, the most important of which has been in the field of medicine. Deficiency diseases, rare in most places these days, can usually be promptly cured by vitamin therapy; vitamin K has been of special use to the surgeon in controlling bleeding during and after operations, and so on. Certainly it is true of vitamins that good things often come in small packages, whether from the druggist's shelf or in their natural state.

13

NUCLEIC ACIDS

THE THREADS OF LIFE

LIVING ORGANISMS cannot survive without a group of special chemicals known as *nucleic acids*. These important molecules control the physical characteristics which are passed from generation to generation. They determine whether an organism will be a bacterium or a plant or an animal; whether a person will have blue eyes or brown, black hair or blonde; and so on.

Nucleic acids are also responsible for a biological nuisance—*viruses*. Many viruses are nothing more than bags of protein filled up with infectious nucleic acid. They attach to healthy cells and "squirt" the nucleic acid into the cell. The virus nucleic acid then proceeds to disrupt the normal metabolic reactions of the cell, often killing it. The over-all result is usually seen as a virus disease, such as polio where irreplaceable nerve cells are killed, causing paralysis.

In order for us to appreciate the biochemical role of nucleic acids, we need to know a little bit about the science of genetics which was founded in the middle nineteenth century by Gregor Johann Mendel. This Augustinian monk was deeply moved by the theories of evolution advanced by Darwin in his book, *The Origin of Species*. He was curious about the differences between the plants in the monastery garden of Brünn, Austria, and he wondered whether he could produce some of these variations by fertilizing them artificially.

Father Mendel chose a pea plant for his first experiments because it could be self-pollinated, that is, the egg cells of a plant could be fertilized with its own pollen. Furthermore, the pea plants clearly differed in several ways. For example, some plants were short and bushy, others were tall and rangy.

For one set of experiments, Mendel chose tall plants and short plants. When he self-pollinated these two strains, with no chance of cross-breeding, the plants yielded seeds which were true to form: Self-pollinated seeds from tall plants grew into tall plants while seeds from short plants grew into short plants. The results never varied; there were never any medium sized plants. Then he fertilized the seeds from some short plants with pollen from tall plants. He planted the *cross-fertilized* seeds and waited for them to grow. Probably, he expected to see both tall and short plants, but to his surprise they were all tall.

He set up his next experiment to determine if it made any difference which plant was used for pollen and which was used to produce seeds. This time he reversed the process of pollination and used a short plant for pollen and a tall one for seed production. The results were the same as before—all the plants were tall. Many men would have given up at this point, but not Mendel. When the seeds from these second generation talls were self-pollinated and allowed to grow both tall and short plants were produced. "What a discovery," thought Mendel. "The self-pollination of plants which look alike gives both tall and short offspring." Carefully he recorded the results of many plantings. The grandchildren always appeared in a ratio of one short plant for each three tall ones. It was clear that tallness and shortness were heritable traits which could be passed from generation to generation.

Mendel's explanation of his results, translated into modern terms, postulates the existence of a basic unit of heredity, the *gene*. Each physical trait—tallness, flower color and so on—is determined by *two* genes, *one from each parent*. One gene is carried by the pollen (male) and one by the seed (female). When fertilization occurs, these two genes pair off to determine some particular trait. The self-pollinated plants which always grow true to form have only one type of gene—either tall or short, but not both.

When self-fertilization occurs (A in diagram) only

one combination of genes from the pollen and seed is possible—tall-tall (TT) to give a tall plant or short-short (SS) to give a short plant. However, when cross-pollination occurs (B in diagram) combination of a gene from the pollen and a gene from the seed gives a new type of fertilized seed. From the diagram you can see that no matter how the genes are combined, the fertilized seed will contain one tall gene and one short gene. This seed is called a *hybrid* which means it is a mixture of tall and short. But tall genes always *dominate* short in peas and so these hybrid seeds always grow into tall plants.

Since seeds or pollen from the hybrid plant can have either one of these genes, but not both, two types of seeds (T or S) and two types of pollen (T or S) will be produced. When fertilization occurs (C in diagram), recombination of genes can occur in four ways. A seed with a tall gene can combine with pollen containing a tall gene (to give TT) or a short gene (to give TS). In a similar way, a seed with a short gene can combine with a tall pollen gene (giving TS) or a short gene (giving SS). The end result of this reshuffling of genes is *three* types of fertilized seeds, TT, TS, and SS, and since T dominates S, only SS will produce short plants. From the diagram you can see that if the combination of genes is a completely random process, there will be three tall plants for every short plant, just as Mendel found.

Mendel drew many conclusions about heritable traits from his carefully controlled studies and these conclu-

MENDEL'S SWEET PEA EXPERIMENT

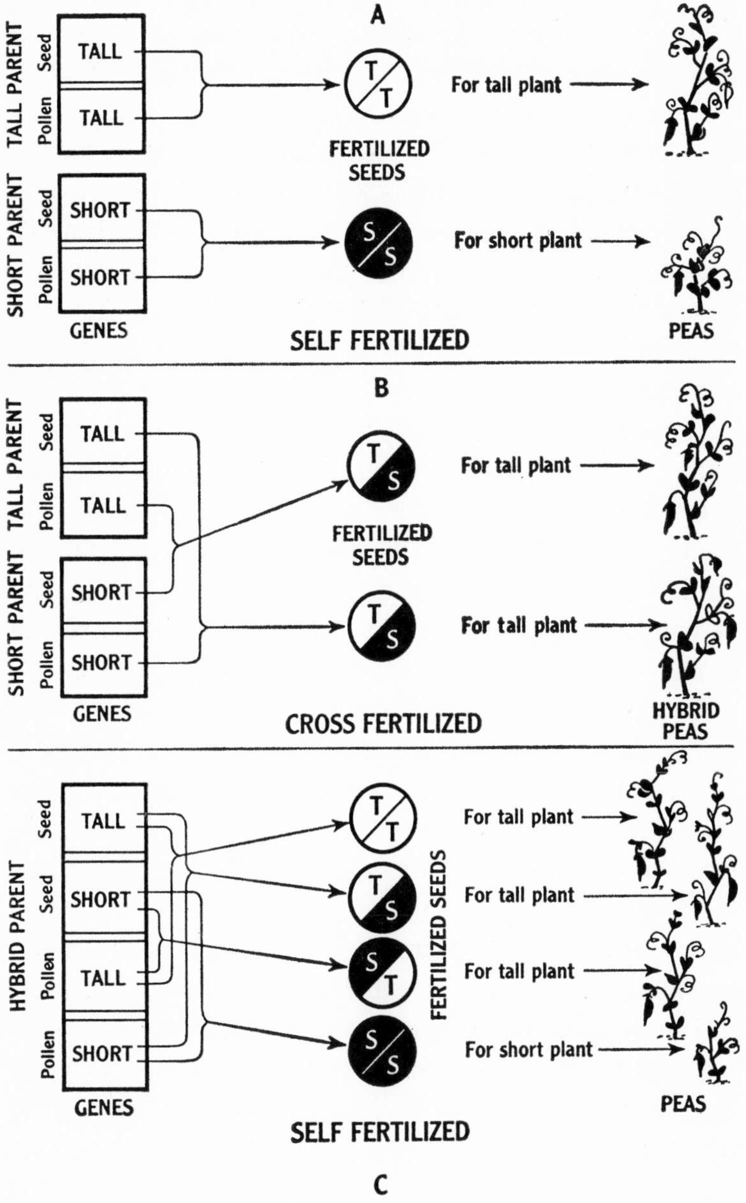

sions came to be known as the *Mendelian Laws* of heredity. Of his work, Father Mendel said, "These [plants] are my children. If I do my artificial crossings, I only copy what wind and bees are doing in nature every day. I don't see any evolution when I look upon the wild flowers and animals, maybe because it is a slow process which needs thousands of years. But I think I can watch evolution among our garden flowers. When the different species and varieties are crossed, new variations arise again and again."

Unfortunately, none of Mendel's scientific contemporaries realized the significance of his work and his forty-four page monograph published in a local scientific journal was forgotten for almost thirty-five years. He used to say, "My time will come." And it did, but not until 1900, sixteen years after his death. But he willed to mankind the basic laws of heredity and shaped the tools for the later studies in the science of genetics.

Of course, Mendel didn't see genes, nor have present-day scientists. But cytologists have observed thread-like structures, called *chromosomes,* in the nucleus of the cell. The chromosomes are supposedly built up by linking genes together much as one would make a string of beads. Under a good microscope we can see the chromosomes quite clearly and in certain organisms we can actually distinguish different types. The egg of a female fruit fly, for example, has a straight x-chromosome while the sperm of the male has either a straight x or a curved y-chromosome. The sex of the fruit fly depends upon which chromosome the egg receives from the father at the time of fertilization. If the egg unites with a sperm containing an x-chromosome, a female fly develops. If the egg receives a curved y-chromosome, a male hatches.

A single chromosome usually determines many characteristics. In the fruit fly, for example, four different chromosomes can be distinguished. These chromosomes carry the genes which determine sex, eye color, wing size, and so on. By doing thousands of crosses with the fruit fly (which conveniently produces a new generation every ten to fourteen days), scientists have been able to map the chromosomes. They can tell, for example, that the genes for yellow wings and white eyes are on the same chromosome and are fairly close together.

The gene is a biological unit. It was invented by geneticists in order to explain the result of their breeding experiments. The biochemist is interested in the chemical unit of heredity, nucleic acid. Two types of nucleic acid are known. One of these, *ribonucleic acid,* or RNA as the biochemist calls it, is present mainly in the cytoplasm of the cell (outside the nucleus) and it appears to be important in protein synthesis. The other type, *deoxyribonucleic acid,* or DNA, is found almost exclusively in the nucleus where the chromosomes are located. In fact, chromosomes appear to be *nucleoproteins* formed by the combination of DNA with special proteins. Most scientists believe that the DNA molecules carry the actual genetic information. If this is true, then genes are made up of DNA molecules.

The most convincing evidence that DNA can transmit

genetic information came in 1944. At that time several different strains of *Pneumococcus,* the bacterium which causes pneumonia, were known. The strain which caused the disease was coated with a capsule of carbohydrate material which gave the cells a characteristic smooth appearance. A non-virulent strain of this organism does not have the capsule coating and is rough in appearance. Here were two easily recognized genetic types, rough and smooth, which displayed different biological activities—one caused disease, the other did not.

Scientists grew cultures of smooth pneumococci (A in diagram) and after a suitable growth period, they broke open the cells and extracted the DNA (B in diagram). Then they added the isolated DNA to a fresh growth medium which was inoculated with a few rough strain cells (C in diagram). The mixture was incubated and the bacteria grew well. When the cells were harvested and examined under a microscope, a large number of them were of the smooth strain (D in diagram). These smooth cells were tested for biological activity and, sure enough, they caused pneumonia. Since none of the smooth strain had been present in the original inocculum (C) the smooth strain DNA appeared to have transformed the rough strain cells into smooth strain. DNA *transforming principle* appears to be a bacterial gene which determines whether a cell will have a capsule or not. When the DNA is added to rough cell cultures, it gets into the cell and directs new generations arising from the

TRANSFORMING FACTOR EXPERIMENT

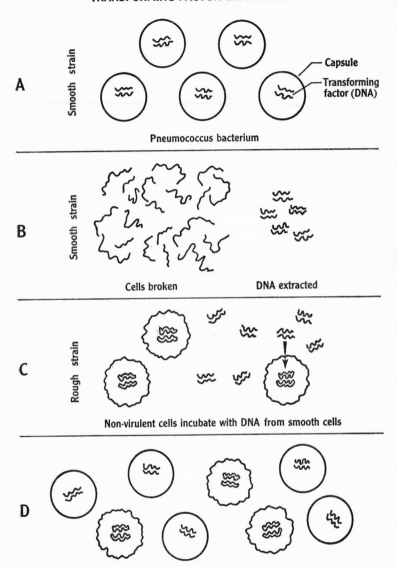

A Smooth strain

Capsule

Transforming factor (DNA)

Pneumococcus bacterium

B Smooth strain

Cells broken   DNA extracted

C Rough strain

Non-virulent cells incubate with DNA from smooth cells

D

Many smooth virulent cells produced

parent cells to form smooth capsules. This process is analogous to the cross-fertilization experiments of Mendel.

Experiments on transforming principle represent a milestone in our understanding of the process of heredity. But how do genes exert their remarkable control over cell characteristics? We do not know the answer to that question; but two biochemists, G. W. Beadle and E. L. Tatum, 1958 Nobel Prize winners in medicine and physiology, have given us a very attractive theory called the "one gene-one enzyme theory."

Beadle and Tatum chose the red bread mold, *Neurospora crassa,* for their experiments. This little mold makes few demands of its environment. It thrives on a simple diet of sugar, water, some salts, and a dash of biotin of the B-vitamin family. Out of these materials it makes everything it needs to live. To accomplish this, it depends upon a large variety of enzymes.

When Beadle and Tatum irradiated cultures of wild type, self-sufficient *Neurospora* with ultraviolet light or X-rays, they found that the cells could no longer make thiamine (a B vitamin) and therefore could not grow unless it was added to the culture medium. Furthermore, if these thiamine-requiring cells were isolated and recultured, the cells which were produced always showed the thiamine requirement. Production of thiamine apparently was a heritable trait. A *mutation* had occurred in which the genetic machinery of the normal, wild type cell had been changed. Somehow the mold had lost its know-how for making thiamine.

Since the synthesis of thiamine, like any other cellular material, is catalyzed by specific enzymes, Beadle and Tatum postulated that one of the enzymes required to make thiamine was no longer present in the thiamine-requiring mutant. Thus, if the process for making thiamine proceeded in steps A→B→C→D→ thiamine, one of the enzymes, let us say the one necessary to convert B to C, was missing, and so the mutant could no longer convert the simple dietary factor A to thiamine.

Beadle and Tatum examined *Neurospora,* and found that all the enzymes for the conversion of A to thiamine can be detected in the wild type, but one of these enzymes is missing in the thiamine mutant just as they had predicted. Since the presence of this enzyme was a heritable trait, they concluded that for each enzyme there is one gene. This concept is widely accepted today. According to this theory, the information which the cell requires to make a specific enzyme is carried in a specific gene within the cell. The implication is that this information is actually carried in a molecule of DNA.

We may view the outward appearance of an organism as the visible result of the functioning of one or another sequence of enzyme reactions. For instance, brown eyes are brown because a brown compound has been synthesized by a collection of cells in the iris. When these cells fail to produce this pigment, blue eyes result. Red hair, too, is a result of the enzyme-engineered synthesis of red pigment in hair. The same is true of skeletal type, blood group, and many other traits. Thus, the presence or absence of specific enzymes appears to determine these characteristics we call traits, and the formation of these enzymes is, in turn, dependent upon the genetic information carried by DNA. But we don't know how this information is passed from DNA to enzyme synthesis.

Virus research has provided additional evidence that DNA acts as a genetic unit by controlling the metabolism of a cell. Consider *bacteriophage,* the viruses which attack bacteria. Those which have been studied most thoroughly are bags of protein filled with DNA. Since they have no metabolic system, they cannot exist by themselves. They are what we call *obligate parasites,* that is, they require a host cell to exist. They use the metabolic reactions of the host to make new bacteriophage.

One of the most carefully studied bacteriophages looks a little like a tiny polliwog (an electron microscope is necessary to see these viruses). It attaches to the bacterial cell by its tail (A in diagram) and squirts DNA into the cell (B). This phage DNA is like the tall genes in Mendel's pea plants because it appears to dominate completely the cell metabolism once it has gained access to the cell. Production of normal cell protein and DNA stops and the metabolic reactions of the cell appear to be diverted entirely into making new bacteriophage (C). When 150 to 300 new phage have been manufactured,

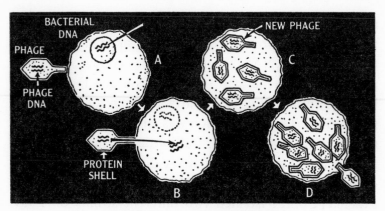

PRODUCTION OF BACTERIOPHAGE

the bacterial cell bursts, liberating the phage and the insidious cycle begins again.

One can think of phage DNA as chromosomes which carry genetic information into the bacterial cell and direct the formation of new viruses. But we don't know how the virus DNA manages to take over completely the normal cell metabolism and use it to produce viruses.

Not all viruses contain DNA. The plant viruses, such as tobacco mosaic virus (TMV), and some animal viruses, such as polio virus, contain ribonucleic acid (RNA) instead of DNA. The RNA is coated with protein, and the finished virus, in the case of TMV, looks very much like a cigarette with the paper carefully peeled off.

Recently it has been possible to separate the protein and the RNA in TMV, and only the RNA appears to be necessary for infection of a tobacco plant. Like bacteriophage, the protein coat of TMV appears to protect the infectious RNA. Under the proper conditions, TMV protein can be separated from its RNA and then recombined to form a new virus particle which looks just like the original. This information was all Dr. Heinz Fraenkel-Conrat at the University of California's Virus Laboratory needed to show that TMV-RNA directed the formation of its protein coat just as DNA did in bacteriophage. Fraenkel-Conrat isolated two different strains of TMV which he could easily distinguish by the type of lesion they produced when they infected tobacco plants. For our purposes, let us call these strains I and II. Then he separated the protein from the RNA and found that he could distinguish the protein of strain I from that of strain II by immunological tests. He also found that he could recombine the protein and nucleic acid and produce an infectious virus particle.

In the next step, the protein was separated from the nucleic acid in both strains. Then, instead of recombining them in the normal manner, Fraenkel-Conrat performed a crossing experiment. He recombined strain I protein with strain II nucleic acid (B in diagram). Now the strain II RNA had a strain I protein coat (B). This recombined, hybrid virus was rubbed on the leaves of a tobacco plant, and the agonizing wait for lesions to appear began. Finally, the leaves broke out in spots characteristic of strain II—the nature of the lesion appeared to be determined

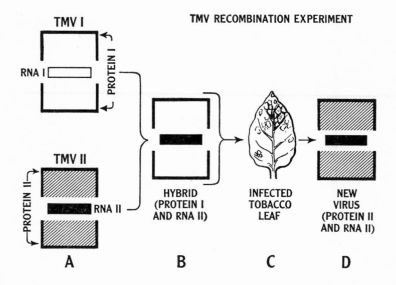

TMV RECOMBINATION EXPERIMENT

TMV I

RNA I

PROTEIN I

TMV II

PROTEIN II

RNA II

HYBRID
(PROTEIN I
AND RNA II)

INFECTED
TOBACCO
LEAF

NEW
VIRUS
(PROTEIN II
AND RNA II)

A   B   C   D

by the RNA. When the virus was isolated from the infected
leaves (C) and carefully examined, they were found to
have strain II RNA, as expected, but even more exciting,
they also had strain II protein coats (D). Thus, the RNA
had not only directed the plant cells to make strain II
RNA, but also strain II protein, so most of the viruses produced were like normal strain II viruses.

Finally Fraenkel-Conrat found that the RNA *alone* was
infectious. When plants were infected with strain I RNA,
devoid of protein, complete viruses were produced in the
plant cells and these viruses always had the protein coats
characteristic of strain I. Apparently, the nucleic acid
gets into the cell and tricks it into making more virus

RNA, instead of normal plant RNA. The virus RNA then directs the cell to make the virus protein and the protein wraps up around the nucleic acid producing a finished virus. This process continues until the cell dies, liberating many new virus particles to attack healthy cells.

Virus research offers the scientist a powerful tool in his struggle to understand the chemical basis of heredity, and the nature of virus disease. For example, it offers the best hope at present for samples of nucleic acids which are pure enough for structural studies. Before we can hope to understand the biological properties of nucleic acids we must know their chemical structure, just as we must know the chemical structure of proteins before we can understand their role as enzymes. Nucleic acids, like proteins, are giant molecules, but the basic building blocks are complicated molecules called *nucleotides,* instead of relatively simple amino acids. The chains of nucleotides are so long in many nucleic acids (as many as 30,000 nucleotides) that it is difficult to see how chemists are going to decipher the sequence. Of course, before they can even begin to study nucleotide sequence, they must have a sample of nucleic acid in which virtually all the molecules are the same. No one has even come close to obtaining such a homogeneous sample. Part of the difficulty lies in the fact that nucleic acid molecules are very fragile, and they are easily damaged during isolation from the cell. However, the biggest problem has been that the chemical properties of nucleic acid molecules with different biological functions are so similar that chemists have been unable to separate them. Since viruses are relatively easy to isolate in pure form and since they are presumably pure nucleic acid surrounded by protein, biochemists have used them extensively in attempts to obtain homogeneous nucleic acid. For some reason which is not understood, these attempts have not been successful so far, but viruses still appear to be a hopeful source of pure nucleic acid.

Virus disease, of course, is still one of man's greatest enemies. Plant viruses alone claim 45 million pounds of tobacco a year in the United States. The California sugar beet grower gave up 10,000 acres of his crop in one year because of curly-top virus. The animal viruses which cause diseases such a measles, polio, and the common cold are well known to all of us.

As W. M. Stanley, Director of California's Virus Laboratory and Nobel Prize winner, aptly put it, "It is obvious that sometime in the future the destiny of every human being on this earth may be affected as a result of the knowledge gained through the study of viruses."

Ninety years have passed since Frederich Miescher discovered nucleic acids and we are just beginning to understand the true significance of this important class of biochemicals. Today nucleic acid research is one of the most active and exciting fields in biochemistry. Part of the excitement was provided by two American biochemists, Dr. Severo Ochoa and Dr. Arthur Kornberg, who were awarded the 1959 Nobel Prize in medicine and physiology for their nucleic acid research.

In 1955, Ochoa discovered an enzyme in bacteria which could make ribonucleic acid. He and his collaborators at New York University College of Medicine isolated the enzyme and partially purified it. When it was mixed with the proper nucleotide building blocks, ribonucleic acid was formed *in the test tube*. As far as they could tell this synthetic RNA was the same as the bacterial RNA which the enzyme normally made while inside the cell. This was a tremendous discovery. Now for the first time biochemists could produce RNA *outside the cell* and study the properties of these remarkable molecules. X-ray crystallographers could take pictures of them to learn more about their structure. But this is only a start. The puzzle of RNA and what it does in the cell is still unsolved even though Ochoa's work has turned up a very important piece of the puzzle.

Shortly after the discovery of the RNA synthesizing enzyme (*polynucleotide phosphorylase* is its name), one of Ochoa's former students, Arthur Kornberg (now at Stanford University), discovered the DNA synthesizing enzyme. Kornberg and his co-workers at Washington University in St. Louis were able to make DNA in a test tube by adding the proper building blocks to a solution containing the partially purified enzyme. Certainly this beautiful work is going to help us understand how the cell makes its genetic material, DNA. In fact, the answers to some of the most puzzling biological questions seem to lie in these remarkable molecules. It remains for biochemistry to close the chasm between genetics and chemistry and to explain how the chemical properties of nucleic acids are related to their biological function.

Chapter 14

ANSWERS
ASK MORE QUESTIONS

OUR STORY has no end—only new beginnings. No question is ever answered without new questions being asked, for the more we learn about this remarkable world of living things the greater our ignorance seems to be. Each answer seems to pose one, two—five—ten new questions which never occurred to us before.

The trail of research is seldom the straight and narrow to the imaginative scientific mind, but a ramification of side trails ever increasing in number as we progress further in our quest of knowledge. Some of the side trails are blind alleys which lead only to frustration and disappointment, but they must be explored because at the end of some of these dark pathways of ignorance lies the light of an important discovery.

Pasteur's studies of the relationship between crystal

structure and optical rotation of the tartaric acids is a case in point. At the time Pasteur began these studies one might easily have remarked, "Why bother with such a trivial thing?" And Pasteur certainly had no idea that these simple but brilliant experiments would form the foundation for a lifetime of research.

The discovery that there were different kinds of tartaric acid which could be distinguished by their crystal structure and by the effect their solutions had on polarized light provided Pasteur with a valuable clue to the cause of fermentation. Remember how he found the optical rotation of tartaric acid solutions changed when they became contaminated with a mold? And he went on to show that lactic acid fermentation as well as alcoholic fermentations required tiny living organisms.

These early discoveries led Pasteur to search for microorganisms as the causative agent in many then mysterious diseases. The results were some of the greatest contributions to society ever made by a single man: finding the cause of silkworm disease and the suggested remedies reportedly saved France's silk industry; the discovery of anthrax bacilli as the cause of anthrax and the development of a preventative vaccine saved countless sheep and cattle from death; development of a rabies vaccine which is still used today and so on. The complete list is a long one, and all of Pasteur's discoveries followed a logical procession of events stemming from his original seemingly unrelated work on tartaric acids.

There are many other examples of important discoveries which were offshoots of some other research path. Büchner was looking for a way to preserve yeast juice for medicinal use in humans when he discovered cell-free fermentation. Fleming discovered penicillin while studying *Staphlococcus*. When he decided to investigate the mysterious mold which had contaminated one of his culture plates he must have realized that it might be an unprofitable adventure. But he was puzzled and he had to find answers, profitable or not.

Even great discoveries which came along the main road of research, such as Sumner's crystallization of the enzyme urease, or Stanley's crystallization of tobacco mosaic virus, led to many later ramifications. Both Stanley and Sumner spent years studying their crystalline preparations from every conceivable angle, and greatly extended our knowledge of these important classes of biological materials.

One cannot help but be impressed with the progress scientists have made in understanding living organisms. For example, only a hundred years ago microorganisms were virtually unknown; but today they are used as research tools in biochemistry to help us understand more complicated organisms, such as man. We have even put these tiny creatures to work for us making valuable chemicals both for industrial use (for example, citric acid) and for use in medicine (for example, antibiotics).

Very little was known about the metabolism of various foodstuffs 100 years ago. Today through biochemical research, the reactions which are responsible for the breakdown and synthesis of fats, carbohydrates, and proteins, are known in considerable detail. Over 600 enzymes have been discovered which catalyze these reactions, and many of these enzymes have been isolated as pure, crystalline proteins. Knowledge of metabolism has helped to establish the requirements for an adequate diet and it has provided at least partial explanations for certain diseases (diabetes, for example). Furthermore, it has made important contributions to industry, such as the production of glycerol by controlled fermentation.

Vitamins were unknown a century ago, and deficiency diseases were still a serious health problem. Today, the vitamin requirements for man have been worked out in detail. We have even found out how to manufacture these accessory factors and put them into a tiny pill for persons on inadequate diets so that, in the main, deficiency diseases are now rare in most parts of the world. We know how many of the vitamins function in the body.

Hormones were not recognized until the turn of the century. Now we know the chemical nature of most of the hormones, which tissues produce them, and what they do in the body. Today many hormones are produced commercially and are widely used in medicine to restore persons with endocrine disorders to a relatively normal life. Insulin is a good example. Thousands of diabetics live happy lives because we have learned how to produce and use insulin.

One hundred years ago, Mendel was working out his

laws of heredity, and not long after Miescher discovered nucleic acids. Neither had the slightest notion that their work was even remotely related. Now we know that nucleic acids are responsible for transmitting the heritable traits which Mendel observed in his sweet pea experiments. Moreover, they represent the genetic material in viruses. And virus research, in turn, has provided us with many practical end products, such as the Salk polio vaccine.

Yes, progress over the last hundred years has been remarkable. Yet we cannot answer the big question, "What is life?" Even with the vast amount of knowledge available today scientists do not agree on what should be called living and what should not.

It is agreed that animals, plants, and even the tiny bacteria are living organisms. All of these creatures have much in common. They possess limiting membranes which characterize cellular structure. They grow and reproduce and so on.

Even at the more basic chemical level living organisms from man to microbe are remarkably similar. They are mainly water, but they contain protein, carbohydrate, fat, nucleic acids, et cetera. The pattern of their metabolic processes is so similar that a universal plan of biochemical reactions is evident. This greatly simplifies the biochemist's task since he can learn much about complicated organisms, such as man, by studying relatively simple organisms, such as bacteria. For example, he may study the changes in a whole life cycle every few minutes with bacteria. In this way he can learn a great deal about the mechanism of cellular reproduction and passage of genetic information with a fair degree of assurance that the information will provide valuable clues as to how these processes occur in higher organisms.

When we progress to levels below bacteria, we begin to lose the landmarks which by experience we have learned to associate with living organisms. Consider the rickettsia, for example. They appear to possess limiting membranes and so have at least rudimentary, cellular structure. They can grow and reproduce. Some of them are larger than the smallest bacteria. In these respects they are certainly living organisms.

But the rickettsia are obligate parasites, that is, they require living host cells to carry out the metabolic reactions necessary for growth and reproduction. So far it has not been possible to grow them on an artificial medium, as we can do with bacteria.

In fact, we know so little about the biochemistry of rickettsia that it is not certain that the rudimentary metabolic machinery which has been observed is not due to contamination of the preparations with enzyme systems from the host cell in which they were grown. But even if these metabolic reactions are real, they are much less complete than in higher organisms. Presumably this is why host cells are required for growth. The rickettsia make up for their deficiencies by using the metabolic machinery of the host cell. This upsets the balance in the host and the result is disease, such as Rocky Mountain Spotted Fever.

The biggest area of uncertainty concerning the living and non-living is represented by the viruses. Part of the trouble arises from the catch-all term *virus*. Actually, virus means poisonous and in the days of Pasteur it was even applied to bacteria. But the discovery that certain disease-causing agents would pass through filters which could hold back bacteria led to the term "filterable virus." With usage, filterable has dropped out and today we simply say virus.

But viruses are not a homogeneous group. Some of them, such as the *vaccinia* virus, which causes cowpox, resemble the rickettsia in complexity. Vaccinia virus has what appears to be a limiting membrane. It contains fats, carbohydrates, protein, nucleic acid, copper, riboflavin, and so on. It also contains a few of the enzymes which are found in higher organisms. Most scientists who work with vaccinia virus believe that these substances are an integral part of the virus and not contaminations.

The complement of enzymes in vaccinia virus is very simple, however, compared to a bacterium. Presumably for this reason, like the rickettsia, they are obligate parasites—biologically limited to a single life condition—and require a host cell in order to grow and reproduce.

Some viruses, such as tobacco mosaic virus, are even simpler than vaccinia virus. In fact, the most careful work has failed to reveal anything other than protein and nucleic acid in these remarkable particles. They appear to be nothing more than large nucleoproteins. And even the protein seems to be unnecessary for growth and development of the virus. Fraenkel-Conrat's experiments indicate that the nucleic acid of TMV (tobacco mosaic virus) is infectious by itself. Inside the host cell it produces its own protein coat and virus particles which appear identical to the normal virus result.

Should we call these nucleoprotein viruses living organisms? If so we should call chromosomes living organisms for they are also nucleoproteins which carry genetic information. Hundreds of pages have been written on Life and the Living without reaching a satisfactory answer. In fact, the question has been baited in the case of viruses by referring to them as the twilight zone between the living and the nonliving.

Is it really important that we classify viruses as living or nonliving? Does a definition of Life serve any useful scientific purpose? In our opinion it does not—at least at the moment. For it seems unlikely that we can arrive at any definition which will serve any purpose when we do not understand even the simplest system we are trying to define. At the present time it is much more important that we answer questions such as, What is the basic difference between viruses and chromosomes? Why does one nucleoprotein (virus) cause disease and death of cells while another (genes and chromosomes) causes it to reproduce in the normal manner? The only real purpose a definition of life now serves is as a basic premise for an interesting scientific debate.

New and exciting discoveries lie ahead in this and succeeding generations, because so far we have only scratched the surface of understanding the chemical processes which constitute the phenomenon we call Life. In biochemistry, as in all sciences, progress is born of man's curiosity about the world he lives in. But curiosity only asks the question, "Why is this so?" The answers come from scientists through their creative thinking (to devise possible answers to the questions) and experimental ingenuity (to devise ways of demonstrating which of the possible answers is correct).

If we are to progress, then, we need, first of all, good research scientists. Therefore, we must seek out talented students and stimulate their interest in science. We must see that they get the best possible training in the shortest possible time. Secondly, we must have adequate facilities for research, for without properly equipped laboratories, ideas remain only ideas. We would do well to heed the words of Pasteur, "Take interest, I implore you, in those sacred dwellings which one designates by the expressive term: LABORATORIES. Demand that they be multiplied, that they be adorned; these are the temples of the future—temples of well-being and of happiness. There it is that humanity grows greater, stronger, better."

INDEX

INDEX